ENVIRSCI 101

Articles and Study Questions

for Discussions

Can Selfishness Save the Environment?

*Conventional wisdom has it that the way to avert global ecological disaster is
to persuade people to change their selfish habits for the common good.
A more sensible approach would be to tap a boundless and renewable resource:
the human propensity for thinking mainly of short term self-interest*

by Matt Ridley and Bobbi S. Low

John Hildebrand who has lived in the Artesian Valley, near Fowler, Kansas, since he was two years old, remembers why the valley has the name it does. "There were hundreds of natural springs in this valley. If you drilled a well for your house, the natural water pressure was enough to go through your hot-water system and out the shower head." There were marshes in Fowler in the 1920s, where cattle sank to their bellies in mud. And the early settlers went boating down Crooked Creek, in the shade of the cottonwoods, as far as Meade, twelve miles away.

Today the creek is dry, the bogs and the springs have gone, and the inhabitants of Fowler must dig deeper and deeper wells to bring up water. The reason is plain enough: seen from the air, the surrounding land is pockmarked with giant discs of green-quarter-section pivot-irrigation systems water rich crops of corn, steadily depleting the underlying aquifer. Everybody in Fowler knows what is happening, but it is in nobody's interest to cut down his own consumption of water. That would just leave more for somebody else.

Five thousand miles to the east, near the Spanish city of Valencia, the waters of the River Turia are shared by some 15,000 farmers in an arrangement that dates back at least 550 years and probably longer. Each farmer, when his turn comes, takes as much water as he needs from the distributory canal and wastes none. He is discouraged from cheating-- watering out of turn--merely by the watchful eyes of his neighbors above and below him on the canal. If they have a grievance, they can take it to the Tribunal de las Aguas, which meets on Thursday mornings outside the Apostles' door of the Cathedral of Valencia. Records dating back to the 1400s suggest that cheating is rare. The huerta of Valencia is a profitable region, growing at least two crops a year.

Two irrigation systems: one sustainable, equitable, and long-lived, the other a doomed free-for-all. Two case histories cited by political scientists who struggle to understand the persistent human failure to solve "common-pool resource problems." Two models for how the planet Earth might be managed in an age of global warming. The atmosphere is just like the aquifer beneath Fowler or the waters of the Turia: limited and shared. The only way we can be sure not to abuse it is by self restraint. And yet nobody knows how best to persuade the human race to exercise self-restraint.

At the center of all environmentalism lies a problem: whether to appeal to the heart or to the head -- whether to urge people to make sacrifices in behalf of the planet or to accept that they will not, and instead rig the economic choices so that they find it rational to be environmentalist. It is a problem that most activists in the environmental movement barely pause to recognize. Good environmental practice is compatible with growth, they insist, so it is rational as well as moral. Yet if this were so, good environmental practice would pay for itself, and there would be no need to pass laws to deter polluters or regulate emissions. A country or a firm that cut corners on pollution control would have no cost advantage over its rivals.

Those who do recognize this problem often conclude that their appeals should not be made to self-interest but rather should be couched in terms of sacrifice, selflessness, or, increasingly, moral shame.

We believe they are wrong. Our evidence comes from a surprising convergence of ideas in two disciplines that are normally on very different tracks: economics and biology. It is a convergence of which most economists and biologists are still ignorant, but a few have begun to notice. "I can talk to evolutionary biologists," says Paul Romer, an economist at the University of California at Berkeley and the Canadian Institute for Advanced Research, in Toronto, "because, like me, they think individuals are important. Sociologists still talk more of the action of classes rather than individuals." Gary Becker, who won the Nobel Prize in economics last year, has been reading biological treatises for years; Paul Samuelson, who won it more than twenty years ago, has published several papers recently applying economic principles to biological problems. And biologists such as John Maynard Smith and William Hamilton have been raiding economics for an equally long time. Not that all economists and biologists agree – that would be impossible. But there are emerging orthodoxies in both disciplines that are strikingly parallel.

The last time that biology and economics were engaged was in the Social Darwinism of Herbert Spencer and Francis Galton. The precedent is not encouraging. The economists used the biologists' idea of survival of the fittest to justify everything from inequalities of wealth to racism and eugenics. So most academics are likely to be rightly wary of what comes from the new entente. But they need not fear. This obsession is not with struggle but with cooperation.

FOR THE GOOD OF THE WORLD?

Biologists and economists agree that cooperation cannot be taken for granted. People and animals will cooperate only if they as individuals are given reasons to do so. For economists that means economic incentives; for biologists it means the pursuit of short-term goals that were once the

means to reproduction. Both think that people are generally not willing to pay for the long-term good of society or the planet. To save the environment, therefore, we will have to find a way to reward individuals for good behavior and punish them for bad. Exhorting them to self sacrifice for the sake of "humanity" or "the earth" will not be enough.

This is utterly at odds with conventional wisdom. "Building an environmentally sustainable future depends on restructuring the global economy, major shifts in human reproductive behavior, and dramatic changes in values and lifestyles," wrote Lester Brown, of the Worldwatch Institute, in his State of the World for 1992, typifying the way environmentalists see economics. If people are shortsighted, an alien value system, not human nature, is to blame.

Consider the environmental summit at Rio de Janeiro last year. Behind its debates and agreements lay two entirely unexamined assumptions: that governments could deliver their peoples, and that the problem was getting people to see the global forest beyond their local trees. In other words, politicians and lobbyists assume that a combination of international treaties and better information can save the world. Many biologists and economists meanwhile assert that even a fully informed public, whose governments have agreed on all sorts of treaties, will still head blindly for the cliff of oblivion.

Three decades ago there was little dissonance between academic thinking and the environmentalists' faith in the collective good. Biologists frequently explained animal behavior in terms of the "good of the species," and some economists were happy to believe in the Great Society, prepared to pay according to its means for the sake of the general welfare of the less fortunate. But both disciplines have undergone radical reformations since then. Evolutionary biology has been transformed by the "selfish gene" notion, popularized by Richard Dawkins, of Oxford University, which essentially asserts that animals, including man, act altruistically only when it brings some benefit to copies of their own genes. This

2

happens under two circumstances: when the altruist and the beneficiary are close relatives, such as bees in a hive, and when the altruist is in a position to have the favor returned at a later date. This new view holds that there simply are no cases of cooperation in the animal kingdom except these. It took root with an eye-opening book called Adaptation and Natural Selection (1966), by George Williams, a professor of biological sciences at the State University of New York at Stony Brook. Williams's message was that evolution pits individuals against each other far more than it pits species or groups against each other.

By coincidence (Williams says he was unaware of economic theory at the time), the year before had seen the publication of a book that was to have a similar impact on economics. Mancur Olson's Logic of Collective Action set out to challenge the notion that individuals would try to further their collective interest rather than their short-term individual interests. Since then economics has hewed ever more closely to the idea that societies are sums of their individuals, each acting in rational self interest, and policies that assume otherwise are doomed. This is why it is so hard to make a communist ideal work, or even to get the American electorate to vote for any of the sacrifices necessary to achieve deficit reduction.

And yet the environmental lobby posits a view of the human species in which individual self-interest is not the mainspring of human conduct. It proposes policies that assume that when properly informed of the long term collective consequences of their actions, people will accept the need for rules that impose restraint. One of the two philosophies must be wrong. Which?

We are going to argue that the environmental movement has set itself an unnecessary obstacle by largely ignoring the fact that human beings are motivated by self-interest rather than collective interests. But that does not mean that the collective interest is unobtainable: examples from biology and economics show that there are all sorts of ways to make the individual interest concordant with the collective — so long as we recognize the need to.

The environmentalists are otherwise in danger of making the same mistakes that Marxists made, but our point is not political. For some reason it is thought conservative to believe that human nature is inherently incapable of ignoring individual incentives for the greater good, and liberal to believe the opposite. But in practice liberals often believe just as strongly as conservatives in individual incentives that are not monetary. The threat of prison, or even corporate shame, can be incentives to polluters. The real divide comes between those who believe it is necessary to impose such incentives, and those who hope to persuade merely by force of argument.

Wherever environmentalism has succeeded, it has done so by changing individual incentives, not by exhortation, moral reprimand, or appeals to our better natures. If somebody wants to dump a toxic chemical or smuggle an endangered species, it is the thought of prison or a fine that deters him. If a state wants to avoid enforcing the federal Clean Air Act of 1990, it is the thought of eventually being "bumped up" to a more stringent nonattainment category of the act that haunts state officials. Given that this is the case, environmental policy should be a matter of seeking the most enforceable, least bureaucratic, cheapest, most effective incentives. Why should these always be sanctions? Why not some prizes, too? Nations, states, local jurisdictions, and even firms could contribute to financial rewards for the "greenest" of their fellow bodies.

PLAYING GAMES WITH LIFE

The new convergence of biology and economics has been helped by a common methodology – game theory. John Maynard Smith, a professor of biology at the University of Sussex, in Britain, was the first effectively to apply the economist's habit of playing a "game" with competing strategies to evolutionary enigmas, the only difference being that the economic games reward winners with money while evolutionary games reward winners with the chance to survive and breed. One game in particular has proved especially informative in both disciplines: the prisoner's dilemma.

A dramatized version of the game runs as follows: Two guilty accomplices are held in separate cells and interrogated by the police. Each is faced with a dilemma. If they both confess (or "defect"), they will both go to jail for three years. If they both stay silent (or "cooperate"), they will both go to jail for a year on a lesser charge that the police can prove. But if one confesses and the other does not, the defector will walk free on a plea bargain, while the cooperator, who stayed silent, will get a five-year sentence.

Assuming that they have not discussed the dilemma before they were arrested, can each trust his accomplice to stay silent? If not, he should defect and reduce his sentence from five to three years. But even if he can rely on his partner to cooperate, he is still better off if he defects, because that reduces his sentence from three years to none at all. So each will reason that the right thing to do is to defect, which results in three years for each of them. In the language of game theorists, individually rational strategies result in a collectively irrational outcome.

Biologists were interested in the prisoner's dilemma as a model for the evolution of cooperation. Under what conditions, they wanted to know, would it pay an animal to evolve a strategy based on cooperation rather than defection? They discovered that the bleak message of the prisoner's dilemma need not obtain if the game is only one in a long series – played by students, researchers, or computers, for points rather than years in jail. Under these circumstances the best strategy is to cooperate on the first trial and then do whatever the other guy did last time. This strategy became known as tit-for-tat. The threat of retaliation makes defection much less likely to pay. Robert Axelrod, a political scientist, and William Hamilton, a biologist, both at the University of Michigan, discovered by public tournament that there seems to be no strategy that beats tit-for tat. Tit-for-two-tats – that is, cooperate even if the other defects once, but not if he defects twice –

comes close to beating it, but of hundreds of strategies that have been tried, none works better. Field biologists have been finding tit-for-tat at work throughout the animal kingdom ever since. A female vampire bat, for example, will regurgitate blood for another, unrelated, female bat that has failed to find a meal during the night – but not if the donee has refused to be similarly generous in the past.

Such cases have contributed to a growing conviction among biologists that reciprocity is the basis of social life in animals like primates and dolphins, too. Male dolphins call in their debts when collecting allies to help them abduct females from other groups. Baboons and chimpanzees remember past favors when coming to one another's aid in fights. And human beings? Kim Hill and Hillard Kaplan, of the University of New Mexico, have discovered that among the Ache people of Paraguay, successful hunters share spare meat with those who have helped them in the past or might help them in the future.

The implication of these studies is that where cooperation among individuals does evolve, surmounting the prisoner's dilemma, it does so through tit-for-tat. A cautious exchange of favors enables trust to be built upon a scaffolding of individual reward. The conclusion of biology, in other words, is a hopeful one. Cooperation can emerge naturally. The collective interest can be served by the pursuit of selfish interests.

THE TRAGEDY OF THE COMMONS

Economists are interested in the prisoner's dilemma as a paradoxical case in which individually rational behavior leads to collectively irrational results – both accomplices spend three years in jail when they could have spent only one. This makes it a model of a "commons" problem, the archetype of which is the history of medieval English common land. In 1968 the ecologist Garrett Hardin wrote an article in Science magazine that explained "the tragedy of the commons" – why common land tended to suffer from overgrazing, and why every

4

sea fishery suffers from overfishing. It is because the benefits that each extra cow (or netful of fish) brings are reaped by its owner, but the costs of the extra strain it puts on the grass (or on fish stocks) are shared among all the users of what is held in common. In economic jargon, the costs are externalized. Individually rational behavior deteriorates into collective ruin.

The ozone hole and the greenhouse effect are classic tragedies of the commons in the making: each time you burn a gallon of gas to drive into town, you reap the benefit of it, but the environmental cost is shared with all five billion other members of the human race. You are a "free rider." Being rational, you drive, and the atmosphere's capacity to absorb carbon dioxide is "overgrazed," and the globe warms. Even if individuals will benefit in the long run from the prevention of global warming, in the short run such prevention will cost them dear. As Michael McGinnis and Elinor Ostrom, of Indiana University at Bloomington, put it in a recent paper, global warming is a "classic dilemma of collective action: a large group of potential beneficiaries facing diffuse and uncertain gains is much harder to organize for collective action than clearly defined groups who are being asked to suffer easily understandable costs." Hardin recognized two ways to avoid overexploiting commons. One is to privatize them, so that the owner has both costs and benefits. Now he has every incentive not to overgraze. The other is to regulate them by having an outside agency with the force of law behind it – a government, in short – restrict the number of cattle.

At the time Hardin published his article, the latter solution was very popular. Governments throughout the world reacted to the mere existence of a commons problem by grabbing powers of regulation. Most egregiously, in the Indian subcontinent communally exploited forests and grasslands were nationalized and put under the charge of centralized bureaucracies far away. This might have worked if governments were competent and incorruptible, and had bottomless resources to police their charges. But it made problems worse, because the forest was no longer the possession of the local village even collectively. So the grazing, poaching, and logging intensified – the cost had been externalized not just to the rest of the village but to the entire country.

The whole structure of pollution regulation in the United States represents a centralized solution to a commons problem. Bureaucrats decide, in response to pressure from lobbyists, exactly what levels of pollution to allow, usually give no credit for any reductions below the threshold, and even specify the technologies to be used (the so-called "best available technology" policy). This creates perverse incentives for polluters, because it makes pollution free up to the threshold, and so there is no encouragement to reduce pollution further. Howard Klee, the director of regulatory affairs at Amoco Corporation, gives a dramatic account of how topsy-turvy this world of "command and control" can become. "If your company does voluntary control of pollution rather than waiting for regulation, it is punished by putting itself at a comparative disadvantage. The guy who does nothing until forced to by law is rewarded." Amoco and the Environmental Protection Agency did a thorough study of one refinery in Yorktown, Virginia, to discover what pollutants came out from it and how dangerous each was. Their conclusion was startling. Some of the things that Amoco and other refiners were required to do by EPA regulations were less effective than alternatives; meanwhile, pollution from many sources that government does not regulate could have been decreased. The study group concluded that for one fourth of the amount that it currently spends on pollution control, Amoco could achieve the same effect in protection of health and the environment – just by spending money where it made a difference, rather than where government dictated.

A more general way, favored by free-market economists, of putting the same point is that regulatory regimes set the value of cleanliness at zero: if a company wishes to produce any pollutant, at present it can do so free, as long as it produces less than the legal limit. If, instead, it had to buy a quota from the government, it would have an incentive to drive emissions as low as possible to keep costs down, and the government would have a source of revenue to spend on environmental protection. The 1990 Clean Air Act set up a market in tradable pollution permits for sulfur-dioxide emissions, which is a form of privatization.

THE PITFALLS OF PRIVATIZATION

Because privatizing a common resource can internalize the costs of damaging it, economists increasingly call for privatization as the solution to commons problems. After all, the original commons – common grazing land in England – were gradually "enclosed" by thorn hedges and divided among private owners. Though the reasons are complex, among them undoubtedly was the accountability of the private landowner. As Sir Anthony Fitzherbert put it in The Boke of Husbandrie (1534): "And thoughe a man be but a farmer, and shall have his farm XX [20] yeres, it is lesse coste to hym, and more profyte to quyckeset [fence with thorns], dyche and hedge, than to have his cattell goo before the herdeman [on common land]." The hawthorn hedge did for England what barbed wire did for the prairies -it privatized a common.

It would be possible to define private property rights in clean air. Paul Romer, of Berkeley, points out that the atmosphere is not like the light from a lighthouse, freely shared by all users. One person cannot use a given chunk of air for seeing through – or comfortably breathing – after another person has filled it with pollution any more than two people in succession can kill the same whale. What stands in the way of privatizing whales or the atmosphere is that enforcement of a market would require as large a bureaucracy as if the whole thing had been centralized in the first place.

The privatization route has other drawbacks. The enclosure movement itself sparked at least three serious rebellions against the established order by self-employed yeomen dispossessed when commons were divided. It would be much the same today. Were whale-killing rights to be auctioned to the highest bidder, protectors (who would want to buy rights in order to let them go unused) would likely be unable to match the buying power of the whalers. If U.S. citizens were to be sold shares in their national parks, those who would rather operate strip mines or charge access might be prepared to pay a premium for the shares, whereas those who would keep the parks pristine and allow visitors free access might not. Moreover, there is no guarantee that rationality would call for a private owner of an environmental public good to preserve it or use it sustainably. Twenty years ago Colin Clark, a mathematician at the University of British Columbia, wrote an article in Science pointing out that under certain circumstances it might make economic sense to exterminate whales. What he meant was that because interest rates could allow money to grow faster than whales reproduce, even somebody who had a certain monopoly over the world's whales and could therefore forget about free riders should not, for reasons of economic self-interest, take a sustainable yield of the animals. It would be more profitable to kill them all, bank the proceeds, sell the equipment, and live off the interest.

So until recently the economists had emerged from their study of the prisoner's dilemma more pessimistic than the biologists. Cooperation, they concluded, could not be imposed by a central bureaucracy, nor would it emerge from the allocation of private property rights. The destructive free-for-all of Fowler, Kansas, not the cooperative harmony of Valencia's huerta, was the inevitable fate of common-pool resources.

THE MIDDLE WAY

In the past few years, however, there has been a glint of hope amid the gloom. And it bears an uncanny similarity to tit-for-tat, in that it rewards cooperators with cooperation and punishes defectors with defection – a strategy animals often use. Elinor Ostrom and her colleagues at Indiana

University have made a special study of commons problems that were solved, including the Valencia irrigation system, and she finds that the connective thread is neither privatization nor centralization. She believes that local people can and do get together to solve their difficulties, as long as the community is small, stable, and communicating, and has a strong concern for the future. Among the examples she cites is a Turkish inshore fishery at Alanya. In the 1970s the local fishermen fell into the usual trap of heavy fishing, conflict, and potential depletion. But they then developed an ingenious and complicated set of rules, allocating by lot each known fishing location to a licensed fisher in a pattern that rotates through the season. Enforcement is done by the fishermen themselves, though the government recognizes the system in law.

Valencia is much the same. Individuals know each other and can quickly identify cheaters. Just as in tit-for-tat, because the game is played again and again, any cheater risks ostracism and sanction in the next round. So a small, stable community that interacts repeatedly can find a way to pursue the collective interest – by altering the individual calculation.

"There's a presumption out there that users always overexploit a common resource," Ostrom says, "and therefore governments always have to step in and set things right. But the many cases of well-governed and -managed irrigation systems, fisheries, and forests show this to be an inadequate starting point. A faraway government could never have found the resources to design systems like Alanya." Ostrom is critical of the unthinking application of oversimplified game-theory models because, she says, economists and biologists alike frequently begin to believe that people who have depended on a given economic or biological resource for centuries are incapable of communicating, devising rules, and monitoring one another. She admits that cooperation is more likely in small groups that have common interests and the autonomy to create and enforce their own rules.

Some biologists go further, and argue that even quite big groups can cooperate. Egbert Leigh, of the Smithsonian Tropical Research Institute, points out that commons problems go deep into the genetics of animals and plants. To run a human body, 75,000 different genes must "agree" to cooperate and suppress free-riders (free-riding genes, known as outlaw genes, are increasingly recognized as a major force in evolution). Mostly they do, but why? Leigh found the answer in Adam Smith, who argued, in Leigh's words, that "if individuals had sufficient common interest in their groups good, they would combine to suppress the activities of members acting contrary to the group's welfare." Leigh calls this idea a "parliament of genes," though it is crucial to it that all members of such a parliament would suffer if cooperation broke down – as the members of real national parliaments do not when they impose local solutions.

WHAT CHANGED DU PONT'S MIND?

For all these reasons, cooperation ought not to be a problem in Fowler, Kansas – a community in which everybody knows everybody else and shares the immediate consequences of a tragedy of the commons. Professor Kenneth Oye, the director of the Center for International Studies at the Massachusetts Institute of Technology, first heard about Fowler's sinking water table when his wife attended a family reunion there.

Oye's interest was further piqued when he subsequently heard rumors that the state had put a freeze on the drilling of new wells in the Fowler area: such a move might be the beginning of a solution to the water depletion, but it was also a classic barrier to the entry of new competitors in an industry. Oye had been reflecting on the case of Du Pont and chlorofluorocarbons, wondering why a corporation would willingly abandon a profitable business by agreeing to phase out the chemicals that seem to damage the ozone layer. Du Pont's decision stands out as an unusually altruistic gesture amid the selfish strivings of big business. Without it the Montreal protocol on ozone-destroying

7

chemicals, a prototype for international agreements on the environment, might not have come about. Why had Du Pont made that decision? Conventional wisdom, and Du Pont's own assertions, credit improved scientific understanding and environmental pressure groups. Lobbyists had raised public consciousness about the ozone layer so high that Du Pont's executives quickly realized that the loss of public good will could cost them more than the products were worth. This seems to challenge the logic of tit-for-tat. It suggests that appeals to the wider good can be effective where appeals to self interest cannot.

Oye speculates that this explanation was incomplete, and that the company's executives may have been swayed in favor of a ban on CFCs by the realization that the CFC technology was mature and vulnerable. Du Pont was in danger of losing market share to its rivals. A ban beginning ten years hence would at least make it worth no potential rival's while to join in; Du Pont could keep its market share for longer and meanwhile stand a chance of gaining a dominant market share of the chemicals to replace CFCs. Again self-interest was part of the motive for environmental change. If consciousness-raising really changes corporate minds, why did the utility industry fight the Clean Air Act of 1990 every step of the way? The case of Du Pont is not, after all, an exception to the rule that self-interest is paramount.

THE INTANGIBLE CARROTS

Besides, environmentalists cannot really believe that mere consciousness-raising is enough or they would not lobby so hard in favor of enforceable laws. About the only cases in which they can claim to have achieved very much through moral suasion are the campaigns against furs and ivory. There can be little doubt that the world's leopards breathe easier because of the success of campaigns in recent decades against the wearing of furs. There was no need to bribe rich socialites to wear fake furs – they were easily shamed into it. But then shame can often be as effective an incentive as money.

Certainly the environmental movement believes in the power of shame, but it also believes in appealing to people's better natures. Yet the evidence is thin that normative pressures work for necessities. Furs are luxuries; and recycling works better with financial incentives or legal sanctions attached. Even a small refund can dramatically increase the amount of material that is recycled in household waste. In one Michigan study recycling rates were less than 10 percent for nonrefundable glass, metal, and plastic, and more than 90 percent for refundable objects. Charities have long known that people are more likely to make donations if they are rewarded with even just a tag or a lapel pin. Tit for tat.

The issue of normative pressure versus material incentive comes into sharp focus in the ivory debate. Western environmentalists and East African governments argue that the only hope for saving the elephant is to extinguish the demand for ivory by stifling supply and raising environmental consciousness. Many economists and southern African governments argue otherwise: that local people need incentives if they are to tolerate and protect elephants, incentives that must come from a regulated market for ivory enabling sustained production. Which is right depends on two things: whether it is possible to extinguish the demand for ivory in time to save the elephants, and whether the profits from legal ivory trading can buy sufficient enforcement to prevent poaching at home.

Even if it proved possible to make ivory so shameful a purchase that demand died, this would be no precedent for dealing with global warming. By giving up ivory, people are losing nothing. By giving up carbon dioxide, people are losing part of their standard of living.

Yet again and again in recent years environmentalists have persisted in introducing an element of mysticism and morality into the greenhouse debate, from Bill McKibben's nostalgia about a nature untouched by man in The End of Nature to James Lovelock's invention of the Gaia hypothesis. Others have often claimed that a mystical and moral approach works in Asia, so why not here? The reverence for nature that characterizes the Buddhist, Jain, and Hindu religions stands in marked contrast to the more exploitative attitudes of Islam and Christianity. Crossing the border from India to Pakistan, one is made immediately aware of the difference: the peacocks and monkeys that swarm, tame and confident, over every Indian temple and shrine are suddenly scarce and scared in the Muslim country.

In surveying people's attitudes around the Kosi Tappu wildlife reserve in southeastern Nepal, Joel Heinen, of the University of Michigan, discovered that Brahmin Hindus and Buddhists respect the aims of conservation programs much more than Muslims and low-caste Hindus. Nonetheless, religious reverence did not stand in the way of the overexploitation of nature. Heinen told us, "Sixty-five percent of the households in my survey expressed negative attitudes about the reserve, because the reserve took away many rights of local citizens." Nepal's and India's forests, grasslands, and rivers have suffered tragedies of the commons as severe as any country's. The eastern religious harmony with nature is largely lip service.

THE GOLDEN AGE THAT NEVER WAS

In recent years those who believe that the narrow view of selfish rationalism expressed by economists and biologists is a characteristically Western concept have tended to stress not Buddhist peoples but pre-industrial peoples living close to nature. Indeed, so common is the view that all environmental problems stem from man's recent and hubristic attempt to establish dominion over nature, rather than living in harmony with it, that this has attained the status of a cliche, uttered by politicians as diverse as Pope John Paul II and Albert Gore. It is a compulsory part of the preface in most environmental books.

If the cliche is true, then the biologists and economists are largely wrong. Individuals can change their attitudes and counteract selfish ambitions. If the cliche is false, then it is the intangible incentive of shame, not the appeal to collective interest, that changes people's minds.

Evidence bearing on this matter comes from archaeologists and anthropologists. They are gradually reaching the conclusion that pre industrial people were just as often capable of environmental mismanagement as modern people, and that the legend of an age of environmental harmony – before we "lost touch with nature" – is a myth. Examples are now legion. The giant birds of Madagascar and New Zealand were almost certainly wiped out by man. In 2,000 years the Polynesians converted Easter Island, in the eastern Pacific, from a lush forest that provided wood for fishing canoes into a treeless, infertile grassland where famine, warfare, and cannibalism were rife. Some archaeologists believe that the Mayan empire reduced the Yucatan peninsula to meager scrub, and so fatally wounded itself. The Anasazi Indians apparently deforested a vast area.

History abounds with evidence that limitations of technology or demand, rather than a culture of self-restraint, are what has kept tribal people from overgrazing their commons. The Indians of Canada had the technology to exterminate the beaver long before white men arrived; at that point they changed their behavior not because they lost some ancient reverence for their prey but because for the first time they had an insatiable market for beaver pelts. The Hudson's Bay Company would trade a brass kettle or twenty steel fishhooks for every pelt.

CAUSE FOR HOPE

We conclude that the cynicism of the economist and the biologist about man's selfish, shortsighted nature seems justified. The optimism of the environmental movement about changing that nature does not. Unless we can find a way to tip individual incentives in favor of saving the atmosphere, we will fail. Even in a pre-industrial state or with the backing of a compassionate, vegetarian religion, humanity proves incapable of overriding individual greed for the good of large, diverse groups. So must we assume that we are powerless to avert the tragedy of the aerial commons, the greenhouse effect?

9

Fortunately not. Tit-for-tat can come to the rescue. If the principles it represents are embodied in the treaties and legislation that are being written to avert global warming, then there need be no problem in producing an effective, enforceable, and acceptable series of laws.

Care will have to be taken that free-rider countries don't become a problem. As Robert Keohane, of Harvard University's Center for International Affairs, has stressed, the commons problem is mirrored at the international level. Countries may agree to treaties and then try to free-ride their way past them. Just as in the case of local commons, there seem to be two solutions: to privatize the issue and leave it to competition between sovereign states (that is, war), or to centralize it and enforce obedience (that is, world government). But Keohane's work on international environmental regimes to control such things as acid rain, oil pollution, and overfishing came to much the same conclusion as Ostrom's; a middle way exists. Trade sanctions, blackmail, bribes, and even shame can be used between sovereign governments to create incentives for cooperation as long as violations can be easily detected. The implicit threat of trade sanctions for CFC manufacture is "a classic piece of tit-for-tat," Paul Romer observes.

Local governments within the nation can play tit-for-tat as well. The U.S. government is practiced at this art: it often threatens to deprive states of highway construction funds, for example, to encourage them to pass laws. States can play the same game with counties, or cities, or firms, and so on down to the level of the individual, taking care at each stage to rig the incentives so that obedience is cheaper than disobedience. Any action that raises the cost of being a free-rider, or raises the reward of being a cooperator, will work. Let the United States drag its feet over the Rio conventions if it wants, but let it feel the sting of some sanction for doing so. Let people drive gas-guzzlers if they wish, but tax them until it hurts. Let companies lobby against anti-pollution laws, but pass laws that make obeying them worthwhile. Make it rational for individuals to act green.

If this sounds unrealistic, remember what many environmental lobbyists are calling for. "A fundamental restructuring of many elements of society," Lester Brown proposes; "a wholly new economic order." "Modern society will find no solution to the ecological problem unless it takes a serious look at its lifestyle," the Pope has said. These are hardly realistic aims.

We are merely asking governments to be more cynical about human nature. Instead of being shocked that people take such a narrow view of their interests, use the fact. Instead of trying to change human nature, go with the grain of it. For in refusing to put group good ahead of individual advantage, people are being both rational and consistent with their evolutionary past.

Study Questions for Ridley and Low (1993)

1. The article begins by comparing two water distribution systems, one sustainable and the other not. Where are the two distribution systems located, and which one is the more sustainable?

2. How could the people using the less sustainable water distribution system change their behavior to adopt or duplicate the practices that contribute to the sustainability of the "better" system?

3. Ridley and Low offer the two water distribution systems as different ways people have dealt with "common-pool resource problems." What other common-pool resource problems were mentioned in the article, discussed in class, or made themselves obvious to you?

4. Historically, when economists (or sociologists) embrace ideas from biology, have the resulting ideas (or policies) been reliably beneficial to society? Examples?

5. Do most economists and biologists think that people and other social animals instinctively cooperate with one another when faced with the need to share limited resources? Why or why not?

6. What do you think Ridley and Low mean by the rather vague sentence "Many biologists and economists ... assert that even a fully informed public, whose governments have agreed on all sorts of [environmentally beneficial] treaties, will still head blindly for the cliff of oblivion." (p. 2, col. 2)?

7. Under what two circumstances is it evolutionarily advantageous for an animal to act altruistically? (p. 2, col. 2 - p. 3, col 1)

8. In what way do Ridley and Low think that "the environmentalists are... in danger of making the same mistakes that Marxists made..."? (p. 3, col. 2)

9. What are some of the mechanisms (described on p. 3, ¶ 3) that governments means have used with success to encourage environmentally beneficial behavior by individuals?

10. What is a "Prisoner's Dilemma" scenario from game theory? (p. 4, col. 1)

11. If two "players" find themselves in a prisoner's dilemma situation on a single occasion, which they do not anticipate will be repeated, what action(s) do the prisoner's usually take and why?

12. If the players instead find themselves in a long series of recurring prisoner's dilemmas, what does the optimum strategy turn out to be?

13. The article offers (on p. 4, col. 2) three examples of animals that appear to use the same stratagem that proved optimum for a series of prisoner's dilemmas as the basis for cooperation rather than pure self interest. Describe one of these examples.

14. What are the two ways the article describes for avoiding the overexploitation of a shared "commons"? (p. 5, col. 1)

15. What seemed to causes inefficiencies in controlling pollution emissions from a Yorktown, VA refinery using the "command and control" approach investigated by a team from Amoco and the U.S. EPA? (p. 5, col 2, and beginning of p. 6)

16. The article describes (p. 6) three "pitfalls" encountered when trying to privatize a global commons, such as a whale species or the atmosphere. Describe one of them.

17. Under the heading "The Middle Way" the article describes studies by Elinor Ostrom of successful solutions to commons problems in which she found four elements seemed to be present when sustainable solutions were found: the communities were small, stable,

communicating, and concerned for the future. Why did small size and communication seem to help communities achieve solutions to problems of shared commons?

18. What are the two examples cited in the article (p. 8) in which environmental consciousness-raising appears to have yielded beneficial results? How much hope can we draw from these two cases that similar moral suasion will persuade people to give up their gas-guzzlers or increase their rates of recycling?

19. Is moral suasion more likely to encourage sustainable behavior in societies where religions Buddhism, Jainism, and Hinduism foster a reverence for nature? (p. 9, col. 1)

20. What evidence does the article offer to refute the notion that unsustainable resource exploitation only recently emerged as a result of man's "hubristic attempt to establish dominion over nature"? (p. 9)

21. What kind of "tit-for-tat" incentives might be used as alternatives to war or world government encourage countries to cooperate in solving global commons problems? (p. 10)

22. Do you find the authors' conclusion that the tendency of humans to act in their own individual interest cannot be suppressed to be dismaying for our hopes of solving commons problems?

SUBTOPICS:
Finding Mr. Right

Why Be Choosy?

Copycat Birds and
Fish

Sadie Hawkins Day<

SIDEBAR:
What Females Want

ILLUSTRATIONS:
Male & Female
Guppy Behavior

Runaway Selection

**FURTHER
READING**

RELATED LINKS

How Females Choose Their Mates

**Females often prefer to mate with the most flamboyant males. Their choice
may be based on a complex interaction between instinct and imitation**

by Lee Alan Dugatkin and Jean-Guy J. Godin

Picture a man who has a way with the ladies, and a character not unlike James
Bond may spring to mind. He's clever, classy, fearless and flashy-characteristics
that are almost universally appealing to the opposite sex. Throw in the powerful
sports car, and you have a nearly irresistible combination.

That females often flock to the most ostentatious males is not a phenomenon
unique to humans. In many different species, successful males--those that sire
the most offspring--are often larger or more brightly colored or "show off" with
more vigorous courtship displays.

Females tend to be the choosier sex when it comes to selecting a mate, partly
because males can produce millions of sperm, whereas females' eggs are few
and far between. Thus, females may be more selective because they have more
invested in each gamete and in the resulting offspring. And because the
availability of eggs is a limiting factor in reproductive success, males tend to
compete for female attention and not vice versa.

Charles Darwin was the first to propose that
competition for mates plays an important role in
reproductive success--a process he dubbed sexual
selection. In *The Descent of Man*, and Selection in
Relation to Sex, published in 1871, Darwin
hypothesized that any trait that gives a male mating
and fertilization advantages will evolve in a
population because males with such traits will
produce more offspring than their competitors.
Assuming the trait is heritable, offspring expressing
the beneficial trait will, in turn, achieve greater
reproductive success than their competitors, and so
on, through future generations. Further, Darwin
proposed that some of these traits may have evolved

GUPPY BEHAVIOR

because they attract the attention of females. The idea that females are
discriminating and can actively choose with whom to mate was controversial
from its inception--perhaps because male-male battles can be quite spectacular.
Males may fight amongst themselves, occasionally in dramatic battles to the
death, to gain mating privileges with females. In comparison, female choice is
generally much more subtle.

Finding Mr. Right

Over the past 25 years, a considerable body of scientific evidence in support of female choice has accumulated. Females actively choose their mates in a large variety of species--particularly ones in which males are less aggressive and display individual differences in secondary sexual characteristics, such as ornamental plumage or courtship displays. Nevertheless, how and why females select their partners and how mating preferences have evolved remain hotly debated issues among evolutionary biologists.

A choosy female faces two general tasks in selecting a mate. First, she must search for and locate a male. This task can be difficult if the population is sparse or if the danger of predators prevents her from spending a good deal of time searching for a suitable mate. Once she has encountered a male, the female must then decide whether to accept or reject him as a mate. The decision often involves some shopping around. In certain mating systems, females may encounter a group of available males and can compare them on the spot. For example, in early spring, male sage grouse (*Centrocercus urophasianus*) aggregate "cheek-to-jowl" in temporary communal mating arenas called leks, where they strut their stuff for the females. A female typically observes the displays of a number of males, apparently comparing them before mating with one lucky suitor. She then leaves the lek to nest and raise her brood elsewhere. Of all the potential mates on a lek, a few preferred males receive the bulk of the female attention.

But males are not always conveniently displayed like chocolates in a sampler box. More commonly, females encounter males one at a time. Comparing males in this case is presumably a more challenging cognitive task, as it involves remembering the characteristics of an individual that is no longer in sight. Studies have shown that females can rank the characteristics of sequentially presented males. Theo C. M. Bakker and Manfred Milinski of the University of Bern in Switzerland found that female three-spined sticklebacks (*Gasterosteus aculeatus*) will tailor their mate choice to the relative attractiveness of the present and previously encountered males. Females were more likely to show interest in a male if his red nuptial coloring was brighter than the previous male's and more likely to reject a suitor whose coloring was less bright than his predecessor's.

Whether a female chooses her mate from among a dozen dancing grouse or between a pair of crimson fish, she generally selects the most conspicuous contender. Empirical evidence indicates that females commonly prefer male traits that most strongly stimulate their senses. (This evidence has recently been reviewed by Malte Andersson of the University of Göteborg in Sweden and by Michael J. Ryan of the University of Texas at Austin and Anne C. Keddy-Hector of Austin Community College.) For example, when given a choice, female green tree frogs (*Hyla cinerea*) are preferentially attracted to males that call the loudest and most frequently; female guppies (*Poecilia reticulata*) to the most brightly colored males; and female mallards (*Anas platyrhynchos*) to males that court them most frequently. Because of such preferences, males have typically evolved exaggerated secondary sexual traits to attract the opposite sex.

Why Be Choosy?

Even though evidence indicates that females can actively choose their mates, the question of why females discriminate, rather than mate at random, remains largely unresolved. How did female choice originate and evolve? What are its benefits and costs to individual females?

In some cases, females may favor mating with a male that is loud or brightly colored simply because he is easy to locate. Reducing the amount of time it takes to find a mate may reduce a female's risk of being killed by a predator. But for many species, mate choice is probably more complex. For many birds and mammals, natural selection appears to favor females who choose mates that provide them with some direct benefit that will increase their fecundity, their survival or the survival of their offspring. Such benefits might include food, a safe haven or even the prospect of fewer parasites.

In a long-term study of the barn swallow *(Hirundo rustica)*, Anders P. Møller of the CNRS in Paris observed that females prefer to mate with males possessing elongated tail feathers. As it turns out, the long-tailed males are infected with fewer bloodsucking mites than their short-tailed counterparts. Because these parasites can jump from bird to bird, females that mate with long-tailed males benefit by avoiding infection and by producing greater numbers of healthier chicks than females that mate with shorter-tailed males. Unfortunately, because selecting a mate that offers direct benefits seems so obvious, few studies have tested this evolutionary model in a rigorous way.

When males provide no obvious resources, such as food or protection, females may choose to mate with the males that appear to have the best genes. How do they know which males have good genes? And why don't males just cheat by faking the traits associated with such genes? In 1975 Amotz Zahavi of the University of Tel Aviv in Israel suggested that females assess only those traits that are honest indicators of male fitness--a hypothesis known as the handicap principle. Honest indicators, which are "costly" to produce and maintain, should be associated with the most vigorous males.

While studying antipredator behavior in the Trinidadian guppy, we recently obtained some evidence that is consistent with the handicap principle. When a predatory fish nears a school of guppies, males, often in pairs, cautiously approach the potential threat to "inspect" it. Such risky behavior has been observed in many species, and behavioral ecologists have suggested that bold males may swim close to a predator to advertise their vigor to nearby females. In fact, laboratory studies have shown that when no females are present, no male guppy plays the hero by approaching the predator more often than his counterpart.

We hypothesized that boldness exhibited during predator inspection might be attractive to females because it should be a reliable indicator of fitness. Less vigorous guppies who tried to "fake" competence in predator inspection would likely be eaten. By using small, custom-built containers that allowed us to position males at different distances from a predator fish, we found that females indeed preferred the most intrepid males. Such courage appears to correlate with color: the males that swim closest to the predator are usually the most colorful. Thus, in the wild, females may have evolved a preference for the flashier males because color is a proxy for boldness and fitness.

Once females have expressed a preference for a certain trait, a process called runaway selection can occur. The model, first brought to the attention of evolutionary biologists by Ronald Fisher in 1958, suggests that a male trait and the female preference for that trait coevolve. For example, females that prefer to mate with large males should produce large sons as well as daughters that show a preference for large males. Under certain conditions, this process can escalate, producing increasingly exaggerated male traits and stronger female preference for those traits.

A number of behavioral ecologists have found some evidence for runaway coevolution of orange body coloration in male guppies and of female preference for this male trait. But a more convincing example of runaway selection has recently been presented by Gerald S. Wilkinson and Paul Reillo of the University of Maryland in their study of the stalk-eyed fly (Cyrtodiopsis dalmanni). In this species, females generally prefer to mate with males possessing widely spaced eyes. By selectively breeding the flies for 13 generations, Wilkinson and Reillo generated one line of flies in which the males had large eyestalks and another line of shorter-stalked males. They found that females in each line preferred the male trait selected for in that line--that is, females from the large-stalk line preferred males with the longest stalks, and females from the short-stalk line preferred shorter-stalked males. Female preference thus coevolved with the selected male trait.

How do preferences about mate choice originate? In some cases, females may have a preexisting sensory bias for a certain trait, not because it represents anything but because it attracts attention--a hypothesis championed most prominently by Ryan and John Endler of James Cook University in Australia. For example, female swordtails (Xiphophorus helleri) prefer males with long "swords" on their tail fins. And although males of a related species--the platyfish Xiphophorus maculatus-lack swords completely, Alexandra L. Basolo of the University of Nebraska found that when she attached artificial, plastic swords onto these naturally swordless males, female platyfish showed an immediate, strong and consistent preference for the males with the counterfeit swords. In other words, platyfish females harbored a preexisting bias for long swords, even though swords reveal nothing about the fitness of platyfish males.

These evolutionary models may be operating separately or in conjunction; it is difficult to untangle them experimentally. Female guppies, for instance, may be partial to orange males because bright coloring is a proxy for boldness or for good health (males with the brightest pigments are probably eating well). But the preference could have originated because females are more attuned to colors of a particular wavelength and then further evolved through a runaway mechanism.

All these models assume that female preference is genetically determined. Recent studies indicate, however, that social factors, such as imitation, also influence mate choice.

Copycat Birds and Fish

Some guys get all the girls. On a crowded grouse lek, for example, the top male may receive 80 percent of the mating opportunities. Is he simply irresistible? Or do females take one another's choices into account when selecting a mate? In the early 1990s a group of Scandinavian researchers, led by Jacob Höglund and Arne Lundberg of Uppsala University and Rauno Alatalo of Jyväskylä University, initiated a detailed study of mate-choice copying in the black grouse (Tetrao tetrix). Using stuffed dummies to represent interested females, the researchers showed that female grouse mated preferentially with the male that appeared to have other females in his territory.

Why copy? Perhaps imitation teaches females what to look for in a male. In an extensive series of experiments on mate-choice copying in guppies, we determined that young females are more likely to copy the mate choice of older, more experienced females than vice versa. Further, copying may save time.

Relying on the judgment of others may allow a female to assess a potential mate quickly and efficiently, leaving her more time to forage for food or hide from predators.

For species in which females copy, a fascinating question emerges: How much of female mate choice is based on instinct and how much on imitation? To tease apart the relative contributions of genetic and social factors involved in mate choice in guppies from the Paria River in Trinidad, one of us (Dugatkin) carried out a behavioral "titration" experiment. First, a female guppy was allowed to choose between two males that differed in the amount of orange that covered their bodies. As expected, females virtually always chose the more orange of a pair of males. Then a copying opportunity was staged, in which the test female was allowed to observe another female apparently choosing the less orange male as her putative mate.

RUNAWAY SELECTION

Which male did she then choose for herself? Remember that the female's genetic predisposition is "pulling" her toward the more orange male, but social cues and the potential to copy are tugging her toward the drabber male. In the end, her choice depended on how much the males differed in coloration. When the paired males differed by small (12 percent) or moderate (25 percent) amounts of orange, the female consistently chose the less orange of the two. In this case, the female succumbed to peer pressure, her tendency to copy overriding her genetic preference for orange males. If, however, the males differed by a large amount (40 percent) of orange, the female ignored the seemingly bad advice and chose the more orange male, her genetic predisposition masking any copying effects.

It appears as if there exists in guppies a color threshold, below which social cues steer female mate choice and above which genetic factors predominate. Dugatkin is performing further experiments to assess whether copying behavior in guppies is itself heritable. Although imitation appears to be based on social cues, perhaps genes govern the likelihood that a female guppy will engage in copying behavior.

Sadie Hawkins Day

Although people are more complex than guppies and grouse, some of the same mate-choice rules may apply to human dating games. According to popular wisdom, it is human females who are the choosier sex when it comes to selecting a mate. As a species, humans meet the criteria for female choice: men, for the most part, will avoid fighting to the death for the hand of a young maiden. And females can distinguish between various males on the basis of differences in their characteristics: some men are brasher, some are brighter and some have bigger bank accounts.

Women may even engage in mate-choice copying. After all, imitation is important in many types of human learning. To determine whether copying plays a role in how women rate a man's attractiveness, Dugatkin is currently collaborating with social psychologists Michael Cunningham and Duane Lundy of the University of Louisville. Although their results are preliminary, they find that women are more likely to express an interest in going out with a man if they are told that other women also find him attractive.

Of course, evolutionary theory will never be able to explain fully singles bars, personal ads or cyber-romance. Even for animals, it appears that the benefits and costs of being choosy when selecting a mate differ for different species, in different environments and sometimes at different times of day. In any case, if animals as simple as guppies can consider the opinions of their peers when choosing a mate, imagine how complex the cues must be that guide humans in their search for the perfect mate.

Related Links

Why Female Flies Fall For Long Eyes

Sexual Selection and the Biology of Beauty

Sexual Selection

Further Reading

SEXUAL SELECTION. M. Andersson. Princeton University Press, 1994.

INTERFACE BETWEEN CULTURALLY BASED PREFERENCES AND GENETIC PREFERENCES: FEMALE MATE CHOICE IN *Poecilia reticulata*. L. A. Dugatkin in *Proceedings of the National Academy of Sciences* USA, Vol. 93, No. 7, pages 2770-2773; April 2, 1996.

FEMALE MATING PREFERENCE FOR BOLD MALES IN THE GUPPY, *Poecilia reticulata*. J.-G. J. Godin and L. A. Dugatkin in *Proceedings of the National Academy of Sciences* USA, Vol. 93, No. 19, pages 10262-10267; September 17, 1996.

SEX, COLOR AND MATE CHOICE IN GUPPIES. Anne E. Houde. Princeton University Press, 1997.

SEXUAL SELECTION AND MATE CHOICE. M. Ryan in *Behavioural Ecology: An Evolutionary Approach.* Fourth edition. Edited by J. R. Krebs and N. B. Davies. Blackwell Science, 1997.

The Authors

LEE ALAN DUGATKIN and JEAN-GUY J. GODIN first joined forces in Trinidad, where they became fascinated by the mating behavior of guppies. An evolutionary biologist, Dugatkin has been an assistant professor of biology at the University of Louisville since 1995. He received his Ph.D. in biology from the State University of New York at Binghamton in 1991. His research interests include the evolution of cooperation and altruism and the interaction of genetic and social factors in shaping behavior. Godin, a behavioral ecologist, is professor of biology at Mount Allison University in New Brunswick, Canada, where he has been on the faculty since 1981. He received his doctorate in zoology from the University of British Columbia and has been a visiting fellow at the University of Oxford. His research focuses on the behavioral ecology of antipredator, foraging and mating decisions in animals.

These questions accompany the article entitled *"How Females Choose Their Mates"* by L. A. Dugatkin and J.-G. J. Godin (1998).

1. How do the differences in the investment made in male and female gametes (i.e. sperm and eggs) influence competition and "choosiness" in mate selection? (p. 1)

2. Please offer one or more other ways in which an act of mating potentially costs a female lek-breeding mammal (cf. p. 2, para. 2) far more resources than it would a male of the same species.

3. Why might the idea that "females are discriminating and can actively choose with whom to mate" have been so controversial when Darwin first proposed it in 1871? Try to think of some other reasons besides the point mentioned in the article about male-male battles. (p. 2)

4. Are approximately equal numbers of males and females more beneficial for successful reproduction by populations of animals that form tight pair-bonds between mated males and females or in non-pair-bonding lek-breeders or polygamous species.

5. In species with characteristically very low population densities, it may be necessary for one sex or the other to advertise itself by bright coloration or loud calls as available for mating, even though such advertisement greatly increases the odds of being targeted by a predator. In a non-pair-bonding species, individuals of which sex are, in a sense, more expendable and therefore the better choice to put at risk? Why? (p. 3, para. 1)

6. According to the authors, what is the major evolutionary goal of females when they engage in careful selection of a mate? (p. 3, para. 1)

7. (Re: Zahavi's "handicap principle", p. 3) Why would bright coloration in birds or guppies constitute a kind of handicap?

8. How does the color of male animals function as a "proxy" for other traits that indicate high fitness? (p.3, 4)

9. (Puzzle question; answer not in article.) Male Birds of Paradise (a family containing mostly non-pair-bonding species) during the breeding season have brilliantly colored (gorgeous) plumage that is so extended and enlarged that the birds have difficulty flying. What do you think happens to the plumage of these males at the end of the breeding season? (*Hint. Do male guppies play chicken with predators when no females are watching, p. 3 para. 4?*)

10. How does the color of male animals function as a "proxy" for other traits that indicate high fitness? (p.3, 4)

11. (Puzzle question.) The bright coloration or risk-taking behavior exhibited by many male animals can be coded for by genes that can be inherited by either their sons alone or (for other mutations) both their sons and daughters. Would it be more selectively advantageous for a female animal to mate with a male whose high-risk characteristics could be inherited only by her sons or by both her sons and daughters? Explain.

12. (Puzzle question.) Many species of non-pair-bonding birds have males with conspicuous bright plumage that makes it easy for predators to see them. Do think it likely that populations of these species that become isolated on islands with no predators contain males that are more spectacularly colored or more drab than counterparts on nearby predator-containing continents? Explain.

13. What other reason do the authors suggest might favor bright-colored males? (p. 4)

14. What did Dugatkin do to try to examine the relative roles of genetic and social factors in the mate choices of female guppies? What did he discover? How might the "criteria" for female guppy mate choice that he found be advantageous for guppies as a species? (p. 5)

15. Describe the process of "runaway selection." (p. 3, 4)

16. To what extent do you think the need to find a mate who will be genetically fit enough to produce successful offspring is at work in human female mate choosing? What about in the US vs. other countries or areas? What about in earlier eras of human history? What other kinds of traits may be or have been more important than physical strength in human mate choices? (p.5)

Encyclopedia of Earth

Should the US be investing time, money, & other resources to limit pop. growth?

Human population explosion

Lead Author: Theodore L. Steck (other articles)
Content Source: United Nations (other articles)
Article Topics: Population *and* Sustainable development
This article has been reviewed and approved *by the following Topic Editors:* Peter Bartelmus (other articles) *and* Arun Sharma (other articles)
Last Updated: May 12, 2007

Table of Contents

1 Introduction
2 Some current demographic trends
3 The demographic transition
4 Why death rates have declined
5 Why birth rates have declined
6 Human population prospects in the twenty-first century
7 Further Reading

is nuclear energy an option the US/world should be pursuing to meet our energy demands?

Introduction

Approximately 6.6 billion humans now inhabit the Earth. By comparison, there might be 20 million mallard ducks and, among a multitude of threatened and endangered species, perhaps 100,000 gorillas, 50,000 polar bears, and less than 10,000 tigers, 2,000 giant pandas and 200 California condors. Notably, the human population has grown nearly ten-fold over the past three centuries and has increased by a factor of four in the last century. This monumental historical development has profoundly changed the relationship of our species to its natural support systems and has greatly intensified our environmental impact. Equally amazing are the signs that, in our generation, the human population explosion has begun to abate (Figure 1; note that, here and below, many of the values given are estimates and, after the year 2005, projections). Our numbers are expected to rise by another 50% before reaching a peak late in this century; a decline is likely to follow. What caused this population surge; what caused its reversal; where are we headed; and how might the proliferation of our species affect its future well-being?

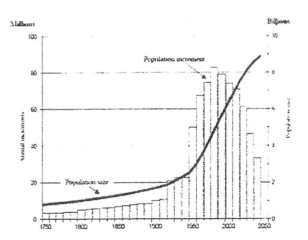

Figure 1. Long-term world population growth, 1750-2050. (Source: United Nations Population Division, "The World at Six Billion")

Some current demographic trends

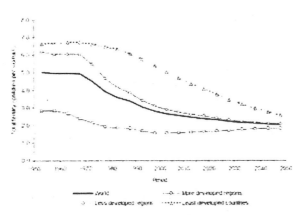

Figure 2. Total fertility trajectories of the world and major development groups, 1950-2050 (medium variant). (Source: United Nations Population Division, "World Population Prospects: The 2004 Revision. Highlights")

Until recently, the growth of our numbers was slow and variable. A pronounced expansion began with the advent of the Industrial Revolution, about two centuries ago. Whereas tens of thousands of years passed before our species reached the one billion mark, around 1800 C.E., it took only 130, 33, 15, 13 and 12 years to add each succeeding billion. This accelerating rate of increase is what is meant by the term population explosion. Around year 1970, population growth reached a maximal rate of about 2% per year—perhaps a thousand times faster than growth in prehistoric times. The annual increment has since dropped from 2.0 to 1.1% (or, as demographers prefer, to 11 per thousand), and it is still going down. Whereas about 90 million individuals were added to the human population at the peak in 1995, our numbers grew by only around 76 million in 2004

(Figure 1). Despite this decline, the world presently takes on a cohort comparable to the population of Germany each year.

Figure 2 shows that fertility is declining with time. It has already declined to below replacement level (i.e., below 2.1 children per woman) in most of the developed countries. World-wide, the average woman currently bears 2.6 live offspring. In some African nations, fertility still exceeds 7 live births. At the other extreme, the average woman in Japan and in much of Europe bears approximately 1.3 live babies. Correspondingly, population growth rates vary with locale, from more than 3% per year in some African nations to a slightly negative rate (i.e., population loss) in some Eastern European states. Among industrialized nations, the U.S. has the highest rates of both procreation and immigration, giving it the greatest overall population growth rate of any industrialized nation—roughly 1% per year.

The average human life-span has risen from 30-40 years in pre-industrial times to about 65 years today (Figure 3).

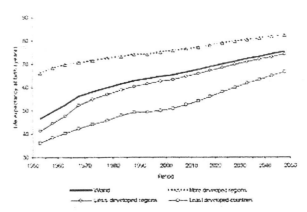

Figure 3. Life expectancy at birth for the world and major development groups, 1950-2050. (Source: United Nations Population Division, "World Population Prospects: The 2004 Revision. Highlights")

Longevity is still not much greater than 40 years in Angola but it is more than double that in Sweden and Japan. In developing nations, longevity has sometimes increased by more than half a year in a calendar year. At the same time, the average life-span has been deflected downward in parts of Africa by infectious diseases such as AIDS and by the sociopolitical upheaval that followed the end of communist rule in Eastern Europe.

The demographic transition

The aforementioned historic trends are well understood. Excluding migration, the rate of change of the number of individuals in a population is the difference between birth rate and death rate. The explosion in human population thus reflects the excess of births over deaths fostered by the Industrial Revolution. Until about two centuries ago, birth rates and death rates were both high. Because these two processes were about equal, the population grew slowly and unevenly. For example, human numbers grew at roughly 0.25% per year in 1700 C.E. Soon thereafter, as discussed below, institutional and technical advances caused death rates to fall in one nation after another around the globe. But because birth rates remained high, population growth rates soared, an unintended consequence of the alleviation of human hardship in the modern era. Then, after a few decades of declining death rates, families in those nations developed the inclination and found the means to dramatically limit procreation. As a result, fertility rates fell, often rapidly, to approach the low death rates, and population growth slowed.

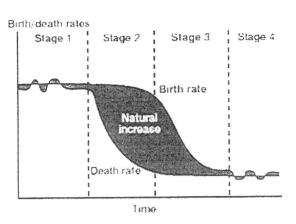

Figure 4. The classic stages of the demographic transition. "Population Bulletin, Transitions in World Population")

A theoretical model called the demographic transition describes the population grows determined by these stages. Figure 4 illustrates its four stages in an idealized fashion. In early times, birth and death rates are high (perhaps both near 5% per year), and there is little sustained growth in the population. In the second stage, death rates decline but birth rates remain high; consequently, the rate of net population growth increases, as indicated in the figure by the shaded area labeled natural increase. Third, birth rates decline to approach the low death rate, causing population growth to subside. Finally, low birth and death rates ensue (each perhaps 1% per year) and growth abates or even becomes negative. The outcome is not a return to the pre-transition state, since the size of the population will have expanded and longevity increased during the demographic transition.

The demographic transition paradigm can be applied both to individual nations and the world population as a whole. The historical prototype is 19th century England. In short order, the transition spread, along with industrialization, to Western Europe and then to the United States. As they modernized in the 20th century, Japan and then certain other Asian nations replicated this transformation. The decades following World War II and the end of the colonial era saw most developing nations embark on this path; now, their death rates are typically at low levels and their birth rates are on the way down. Thus, most nations are currently somewhere in the third stage of their demographic transition and some are in stage four. In fact, the growth rate of the world population in year 2006 was 1.1%, the difference between a birth rate of 2.0% and death rate of 0.9% per year.

In some [[developing nation]s], in which custom may outweigh modern alternatives, the demographic transition has stalled midstream. That is, low death rates (say, 1-2% per year or less) may have been achieved but birth rates linger at 3 to 5% per year. Thus, as in Niger, Mali and Uganda, population growth can exceed 3% per year, making the corresponding doubling time of the population less than 25 years. (Doubling time in years equals 70/growth rate in percent per year. In this example, the doubling time would be 70/3 or 23 years.) This situation can lead to a demographic trap where rapid growth undercuts the very technical, social and economic progress that might otherwise resolve it. The developing nations as a group now have 80% of the world's population and generate 96% of its growth. The on-going increase of world population can therefore be understood to represent unfinished demographic transitions in diverse pre-industrial societies.

Why death rates have declined

Infectious disease has always been a major cause of human mortality. Over the years, these diseases have included malaria, influenza, tuberculosis, cholera, and a variety of parasitic infections. In particular, childhood diarrhea and respiratory diseases of bacterial or viral origin ravage the young in poor nations; infant mortality can amount to more than 10% of the live births in those settings, compared to less than 0.5% in many industrialized states. The battle against infectious diseases gained force early in the modern era through the development of public health regimes. Thus, long before the era of twentieth-century patient-directed medicine, we learned how to avoid the perils of contaminated drinking water, to drain swamps where mosquitoes harbor the malaria parasite, to immunize the young, to quarantine the infected and to teach public hygiene. (A classical example of an early public health intervention was the introduction of vaccination against smallpox by Edward Jenner more than two centuries ago; this scourge has now been entirely eradicated.) In addition, improved nutrition not only saved lives by itself but also strengthened resistance to infection. These simple preventive strategies were inexpensive and colonists brought them along to protect themselves and their workers. Even today, the transfer of readily-available technology and know-how from more developed countries (MDCs) continues to reduce mortality rates in less developed countries (LDCs).

Why birth rates have declined

Children are naturally loved and valued for themselves. But, especially in traditional (i.e., pre-modern) settings, children are also economic assets: a ready source of capital and security when alternatives are out of reach. Sons are of particular value, since it is they who typically inherit both the family plot and the responsibility for caring for aging parents. For practical reasons, daughters are often less desired: they may be regarded as not as productive and as likely to marry and move on, often with a costly dowry payment. Thus, time-honored wisdom might suggest an investment strategy of having, say, eight offspring. Parents can then expect four sons, one or two of whom will hopefully survive childhood and be there to serve with devotion in the distant future. Such views become institutionalized in cultural norms and shared practices.

Under favorable conditions, a woman can bear as many as 20 children though such a high level of fertility has not been observed anywhere. Empirically, the highest level of fertility ever observed has been much less, not more than 11-12 children. It is because parents universally chose to limit family size because too many children present costs in excess of benefits. Many traditional values and practices facilitate procreative restraint. Pregnancy can be avoided by celibacy, late marriage and sexual abstinence; various other precautions such as the rhythm method reduce the risk of conception. Of particular importance is prolongation of the nursing of children. (This is because lactation inhibits ovulation through the mother's endocrine system, thereby thwarting pregnancy.) In addition, desperate measures to control family size are frequently taken by those who lack better options. For example, perhaps 20 million pregnancies a year, more than one-tenth of the total, are ended by septic (criminal) abortion despite serious risks to the mothers. Infanticide is another long-standing expedient. Especially in hard times, the girls are selected against: ultrasound previews, typically illegal, are used in Asia these days to pick out female fetuses for abortion. The various practices favoring male heirs is said to account for "100 million missing women" world-wide.

Just as the Industrial revolution precipitated a fall in death rates with a consequent surge in population, it has also driven the subsequent fall in birth rates and the resolution of that explosion. This is because industrial societies have substituted alternative sources of economic security for large family size. This is not just a wealth effect. Rather, modern countries have elaborated civil institutions that provide a social safety net that makes possible smaller families with greater investment in each individual. The safety net promotes health and education; property rights (ownership) and civil rights (e.g., the vote, equality before the law and public safety); some measure of financial security (e.g., insurance, loans, retirement plans, unemployment benefits, job creation and retraining programs); and income redistribution (e.g., public welfare programs and graduated taxation). Individual aspirations then become

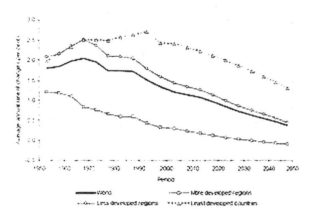

Figure 5. Average annual rate of change of the population of the world and major development groups, 1950-2050 (medium variant). (Source: United Nations Population Division, "World Population Prospects: The 2004 Revision. Highlights")

reoriented from security to self-realization, and from subsistence to productivity, as desperate choices are replaced by good options.

Women in MDCs typically expect to have two children and generally have slightly fewer. In these nations, women tend to marry late—or not at all. Contraception is widespread and the choices are diverse; for example, condoms, cervical loops and caps, vaginal spermicides and surgical sterilizations for both the female and the male. There are also pills to prevent ovulation (i.e., oral contraceptives), to induce the early miscarriage of a pregnancy and to thwart the implantation of a fertilized egg "the morning after." Surgical abortions are common and (quite the opposite of criminal or septic abortion) safer than live births.

Increasingly, individuals in developing nations have become aware of modern lifestyles through education, trade, migration and mass media (including radio or television in the vicinity). Indeed, nearly half of the human population—a steadily rising fraction—now live in cities from which they report trends to those back home. Cultural diffusion has also alerted pre-modern communities (as well as national governments) to the socio-economic burden of high fertility. It has also shown them ways to build social welfare in advance of industrialization and wealth creation (see Kerala). Foremost among these countervailing forces is a couple's anticipation of improved longevity for the members of the family. Similarly, the sense of security of those in poverty increases with opportunities for education, physical and social mobility, economic advance and the accumulation of modest personal savings. The transfer of low-cost know-how and materials from developed nations has greatly benefited the poor. Food security in impoverished communities, while often problematical, has nevertheless risen steadily in recent decades just as infant mortality has fallen. Confidence in one's government also helps. All of these factors have encouraged individuals in LDC to address poverty through personal and social measures that, among other effects, supplant the predisposition to large families. Economic development can then follow. As a result, population growth is declining in all parts of the world (Figure 5).

The empowerment of women (e.g., their literacy and employment) has been of special importance, as have international efforts to provide family planning assistance and contraception where needed. The steady decline of LDC fertility and population growth documents the impact of these processes (Figures 2 and 5). Nevertheless, more than 300 million women in LDC presently express the unfulfilled desire for fewer children and for family planning assistance such as information and contraceptive devices. On the other hand, many traditional mothers still aspire to large families (Figure 6). Thus, the population explosion is far from over.

Human population prospects in the twenty-first century

The overall human death rate is not likely to change significantly in the foreseeable future. It will presumably decline in nations like Russia which have recently suffered sociopolitical upheavals. The opposite trend can be expected for developing nations as their youthful populations age. Globally, birth rates will probably continue to decline in the coming decades since, nowadays, couples are increasingly prone to limit their family size, whatever their wealth. Coercion by national governments, such as China's one-child policy, appears to be unnecessary. If and when the global birth rate again matches death rate, we will hit zero population growth. This could occur by the year 2070 when the population might be 9.5 or 10 billion. Negative population growth may then ensue, as is now looming in an increasing number of MDCs.

Although this is an era of decreasing birth rates, diverse constituencies nevertheless regard procreation as either a good in itself or as a practical imperative. Among these pro-natal voices are the following:

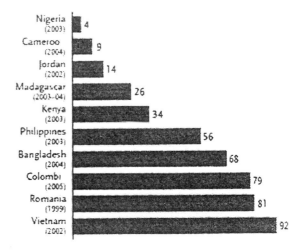

Figure 6. Percent of married women of reproductive age with two living children who do not want another child. (Source: "Population Reference Bureau, 2006 World Population Data Sheet")

1. Standard economic thinking holds that human capital (e.g., labor and intellectual creativity) drives wealth creation; hence, the more people, the better off we are. Such a cornucopian view foresees no limits to an indefinitely expanding economy, environmental impacts notwithstanding. At the same time, many economists anticipate a point beyond which

further additions to our numbers will diminish our well-being.

2. A large fraction of MDC governments would like the demographic profile of their nation to be youthful. Their premise is that the young provide the nation's workforce and army with vitality and strength. In addition, wage-earners provide tax revenues.

3. Those concerned with the well-being of the elderly see that an increasing dependency ratio (i.e., retirees per worker) will increasingly burden national retirement plans, such as U.S. Social Security. (The governments of some LDCs are grappling with the opposite issue: high population growth can undercut their social welfare and economic progress.)

4. Various cultural and religious norms encourage procreation. In some communities, men are expected to show virility by siring a large brood. It is sometimes a mother-in-law's prerogative to press for more grandchildren.

5. Employers may welcome a large labor pool in the hope that competition for jobs will drive down workers' wages.

6. Many in poverty still see their progeny as their best hope in desperate times.

7. With increasing affluence, many parents can afford to value children for their intrinsic worth and enjoy large families.

For these various reasons most MDC governments favor pronatal policies, and many now maintain programs that encourage procreation. In some LDCs the levels of infant and child mortality are still quite high and parnts are afraid to limit family size. They would produce more children than they actually want because of the fear that some may die. Nevertheless, the trend toward decreasing family size continues around the globe, driven mainly by the desires of women to compete with men in all walks of life. This unintended consequence of modernization and globalization is welcomed by those who, like Malthus early in the Industrial Revolution, view overpopulation as a fundamental threat to human welfare. From the field of ecology, with its concern for carrying capacity and overshoot, comes the question of whether humans might exceed the limits to growth in a finite habitat. One way this issue has been analyzed is the calculation of the ecological footprint; i.e., that portion of the ecosphere usurped by the activities of an individual, a group or a nation. Applications of this admittedly imprecise parameter have raised the possibility that our current practices exceed the bounty of this planet and are therefore unsustainable (see sustainable development). Another perspective posits that human impact increases with 1) our numbers; 2) material consumption per person (see Consumption and well-being); and 3) the extent of environmental damage caused by each unit of that consumption. (See the IPAT equation.) Since it seems unfair for the rich to thwart the material progress of the poor, yet politically difficult to reign in the appetites of the affluent and technically challenging to mitigate the impact of their consumption, factors 2 and 3 seem to be less amenable targets (particularly in the poor countries) than curtailing population size as ways to limit our impact. While the Earth's carrying capacity for our species is not known, the precautionary principle advises that it is better to be safe than sorry.

Further Reading

- Ayers, R. 2004. The Economic Conundrum of an Aging Population. World Watch Magazine, 17 (No. 5), 45-49.
- Dasgupta, P.S. 1995. Population, Poverty, and the Local Environment. Scientific American, 272 (Feb), 26-31.
- Dasgupta, P.S. 2003. Population, Resources, and Welfare: An Exploration into Reproductive and Environmental Externalities. In K-G. Mäler and J. Vincent (Editors), Handbook of Environmental and Resource Economics, North Holland Amsterdam, 191-247.
- Demeny, P. 1990. Population. In B.L. Turner (Editor), The Earth as Transformed by Human Action: Global and Regional Changes in the Biosphere over the Past 300 Years. Cambridge University Press with Clark University, Cambridge; New York, 41-54. ISBN: 0521446309
- Demeny, P.G. and McNicoll, G. (Editors). 2003. Encyclopedia of population. Macmillan Reference USA., New York, 2 v., 1040 pp. ISBN: 0028656776
- John Bryant. 2007. Theories of Fertility Decline and Evidence from Development Indicators. Population and Development Review, 33 (No. 1), 101-127.
- Population Reference Bureau. 2006 World Population Data Sheet.
- Transitions in world population. 2004. Population Bulletin, 59 (No. 1).
- United Nations Population Division. The World at Six Billion.

Citation

Steck, Theodore (Lead Author); United Nations (Content source); Peter Bartelmus and Arun Sharma (Topic Editors). 2007. "Human population explosion." In: Encyclopedia of Earth.

Virginia Deane Abernethy

Not Tonight, Sweetie; No Energy

A Neo-Malthusian Looks at Fossil Fuels and Fertility

The "fertility opportunity hypothesis" holds that parents want more children when they perceive forthcoming opportunities for a better life, but have fewer children if they anticipate hard times ahead. Perceptions of a coming global oil scarcity could result in population growing less than the UN expects.

The Reverend Thomas Malthus (1766–1834) was notorious for the view that "positive checks"—meaning poverty, famine, and premature mortality—are the only means of keeping population size in balance with resources. But his second edition of *An Essay on the Principle of Population* is far from pessimistic: it develops the idea that "moral restraint" (encompassing social rules as well as personal decisions) often depresses the fertility rate, thus slowing or stopping population growth before calamities occur.

Worldwide, the dynamics of self-restraint are causing fertility rates to fall much more rapidly than generally anticipated, vindicating Malthus's foresight. Projections of an ultimate population size of 12 billion have been forgotten. In 2003, the United Nations offered a middle projection of 8.9 billion as the ultimate peak world population. A March 2004 report by the U.S. Census Bureau projected a most-likely scenario of 9.1 billion by 2050, with average fertility below replacement level and with hotspots of elevated mortality.

My own view is even more optimistic: world population is unlikely to rise above 8 billion (from approximately 6.4 billion today), and the fertility rate will fall from the Population Reference Bureau's 2003 estimate of 2.8 children per woman to below replacement level within the next dozen years. With population size peaking at a level lower than either the Census Bureau or the United Nations project, much excess mortality may be avoided.

Fertility and Opportunity

Why do I believe this? Because my data show that people faced with real *or perceived* deprivation typically exercise reproductive caution. Whether in hunter-gath-erer or agrarian societies, or developing or industrialized countries, intimations of scarcity (with respect to wants as well as needs) encourage restraint. And in the near term, expensive fossil fuels could trigger an acute sense of scarcity. Put another way, this *fertility opportunity hypothesis* proposes that people usually have as many children as they think they can afford, and that the motivation to have more or fewer arises from perception of economic prospects. Perceptions crystallize through comparisons to past experiences or a reference group.

Where straying above carrying capacity would terminally threaten life-support systems, *individual* evaluation of relative well-being often gives way to rigid, culturally embedded rules. The hierarchical social structure of indigenous peoples living in the Amazonian blackwater ecosystem is illustrative. With sparse game, few fish, and nutrient-poor soils, population size remains in balance with resources because only the few fortunate heirs to fishery and residential sites expect to marry and reproduce. Defined real estate rights are unusual in primitive societies but a less restrictive system might founder as population overshot resources.

The fertility opportunity hypothesis suggests that rules atrophy, reproductive decisions become individualized, fertility rates rise, and populations explode when communities encounter new opportunities, such as those created by potato cultivation in Ireland around 1740, or by nitrogen fertilizer and foreign aid to underdeveloped countries during the twentieth century. Self-restraint is not rediscovered until economic prospects sour.

Anecdotal support for this idea is plentiful. For example, a Cairo slum dweller says, "We're just surviving.... Certain days we don't eat...I don't understand how people with seven or eight children survive." Pondering what she would do differently if she were rich, an Ethiopian mother of five says, "If I were wealthy, say if I had horses and a better house, I'd have more children." A Russian mother of two who has relied on abortion to limit family size muses, "I would have had more children if life were better." Near Mexico City, a Roman Catholic mother of two defends her use of contraception: "Things are difficult here....

Jobs are hard to come by."

Stronger support can be found in a number of case histories, several of which I've summarized below:

● **Rwanda.** The Rwandan population quadrupled between 1950 and 1993. Although designed to help, moves to virgin land and the agricultural assistance given farmers were arguably not constructive in the long run because they promoted a frontier mentality, including idealization of large families. Observes demographer John May, "…the relative availability of land during the agricultural colonization and intensification processes might have been conducive to higher fertility levels."

The fertility rate in 1987, a decade before Hutu massacred Tutsi, was 8.5 births per woman. By 1992, it was 6.2, a decline of more than two children per woman within five years. This ostensibly demonstrated the effectiveness of family planning programs launched some years earlier. As late as 1992, however, only 12.9 percent of married, reproductive-age women used modern contraceptive methods—hardly sufficient to account for the two-child decline in the total fertility rate. May suggests that the actual behavioral change that promoted lower fertility was delayed marriage.

Rwandans became infused with a new sense of caution when gains from intensifying agriculture and dispersing the population ran their course. Subdivision in each generation made family plots too small—by 1984, 57 percent of holdings were less than one hectare—for their many uses, including cultivation, pastureland, and fuelwood. Moreover, droughts increased and marginal land brought into cultivation 20 years earlier was losing productivity. A pervasive image of limits apparently made family formation less attractive, inspiring marital and reproductive self-restraint.

● **Brazil.** Referring to a poverty-stricken region of high effective population density, sociologist George Martine has written, "Brazil's poorest socioeconomic region, the Northeast, has undergone the fastest fertility reduction over the last 20 years: there, the TFR [total fertility rate: roughly, the average number of live births per woman] has fallen from around 7 in 1970 to 3.7 in 1990." Martine observes that the commonly men-

tioned "demographic transition variables," including women's education and participation in the labor force, did not cause the fertility decline. He suggests that the underlying mechanism was an unforeseen aspect of modernization: new expectations set up large sectors of the population for disappointment.

● **Egypt and Morocco.** Philippe Fargues and Youssef Courbage, studying Egypt and Morocco respectively, suggest that fluctuations in household economies affect fertility rates. In both countries, flows of widely distributed new wealth stimulated childbearing. The source

Paul Harrison/Still Pictures/Peter Arnold

Good times ahead? Perceptions of improving prospects may lead to larger families (Brazil).

(private income or government-subsidized housing, food, healthcare, and education) appeared not to matter. Fargue and Courbage concur that modernization—including reductions in infant mortality, better healthcare, education (especially for women), and rising standards of living—were *not* correlated with declining fertility rates and clearly *were not* causally related to them. In both countries, economic retrenchment with increasing disparity between aspirations and reality underlay the fertility decline. Sustained fertility reduction began when governments reduced subsidies, women entered the workforce to make ends meet, and the tax burden on families rose.

In Egypt (which has the longest history of concern over its expanding population of any Muslim country), Gamal Abdel Nasser encouraged family planning programs, and fertility declined during his tenure from 6.7 births per woman in 1960 to 5.0 births in 1970. Nevertheless, Fargue denies that programmatic family planning efforts caused the fertility decline. He cites, instead, new pressures coincident with the economic recession through which Egypt floundered until after Nasser's death. When Anwar El Sadat came to power in 1973, he encouraged domestic entrepreneurial activity, emigration, and foreign investment. He also signed a formal peace treaty with Israel (the Camp David accords) that still brings Egypt $2.5 billion per year in aid from the United States. This aid, along with oil revenues and fees for foreign shipping through the Suez Canal, funded expansion of social programs. Remittances from expatriate Egyptians—which by the early 1980s amounted to US$5 billion a year, the equivalent of 90 percent of Egypt's annual export revenues—augmented income in many families.

These dollar flows contributed, Fargue observes, to "a substantial increase in the standard of living" through el-Sadat's early years. "Now better off, families could more easily satisfy an unchanged desire to have numerous offspring." The fertility rate did indeed spike, rising 30 percent from 1970 to 6.5 births per woman in the early 1980s.

President Hosni Mubarak, successor after El Sadat was assassinated in 1985, inherited a deteriorating economy and was soon forced to scale back social programs and subsidies. Awareness that the historically huge population was causing massive underemployment and shortages in arable land, food, and water became acute. The eroding standard of living apparently gave impetus to preferences for smaller family size. Between 1988 and 2003, the Egyptian TFR declined from 5.0 to 3.5 children per woman. The parallel, downward trends in socioeconomic indicators and fertility rates support Fargues's contention that, "Egypt's demographic transition has been driven not so much by economic development as by its hiccups."

• **Asia.** The nine former "Asian tigers" (Hong Kong, Indonesia, Japan, Malaysia, the Philippines, Singapore, South Korea, Taiwan, and Thailand) vary greatly but each is modern and vibrant in at least one primary sector. During late summer of 1997, the nine tigers temporarily reversed from economic growth to stagnation. The downward spiral began with a 40-percent currency devaluation in Thailand, and quickly spread.

In Japan, unemployment rates in 1998 and 1999 rose to their highest level since 1953. Personal bankruptcies in 1999 were 50 percent higher than in 1997 and, as a further sign of falling incomes, retail sales declined through 1999. In 1998, the Japanese suicide rate was the highest recorded. Contemplating an uncertain future, a majority of university students expressed a preference for government as opposed to private-sector employment.

In print, I predicted that the economic collapse would cause fertility rates to decline at a faster rate during the 1997–1999 interval than during preceding two-year intervals. Fertility was trending downward to varying degree in each country, but I expected steeper declines. And in fact the percentage decline in the 1997–1999 interval proved more than six times as great as the average of declines in previous intervals, a statistically significant difference. In contrast, a comparison group of countries that experienced no particular economic shock showed random variation in fertility rates.

Nearing Limits?

Regarding the future, one searches for factors that could have a decisive effect on perception of economic opportunity and, therefore, fertility rates. My candidate is fossil fuels.

The availability of energy is one of the key influences on the evolution of human culture, and some scholars have even suggested a relationship between energy use per capita and population size. For 21st-century civilization, oil and gas are unparalleled sources of energy, and their penetration into the depths of the economy is profound. Not only is transportation radically dependent on oil; petroleum products are also the feedstock for myriad industrial and agricultural processes. As pesticides and fertilizers, petrochemicals are *irreplaceable* in high-yield modern agriculture. Physicist Albert Bartlett famously said that industrialized agriculture uses land to turn oil into food, and economist John Gever and his colleagues have suggested that by approximately 2020 agriculture will be recognized as the highest use of fossil fuels.

Colin Campbell, a retired oil industry geologist and editor of the newsletter for the Association for the Study of Peak Oil (ASPO), and electrical engineer Richard Duncan were among the first to write that energy price is a major causal factor in economic growth rates. Until relatively recently, however, most public discussions were dismissive. Through the decade of the dot-com bubble—which was favored by very cheap energy for much of its run—one heard instead of the de-coupling or de-linking of oil and economic growth.

Smarter business analysts began to reverse course in late 2002. Martin Wolf, writing in the *Financial Times*, said that "a rise in the price of oil reduces real income and real wealth, squeezes profits, and transfers incomes to oil-producing countries, all of which will be contractionary.... Changes in unemployment have consistently followed changes in the real price of oil...." His article featured a chart showing higher unemployment rates in oil-importing countries lagging higher oil prices by two to three years during the period 1970–2002. Most U.S. recessions since World War II have followed a period of rising oil prices.

High-priced energy depresses business, prolonging recessions or stagflation. Farmers reduce fossil-fuel-based agricultural inputs, substituting organic and no-till methods. Although these methods are theoretically ideal from the perspective of sustainable agriculture, the human cost includes smaller crops and pricier food than with industrial agriculture.

Is such a future upon us? Numerous geologists, physicists, and engineers (including, but not limited to, Colin Campbell and his colleagues at ASPO) calculate that a plateau and then decline in petroleum, natural gas, and liquid natural gas (LNG) production will commence within five to ten years. In 2002, the executive vice-president of Exxon-Mobil publicly revealed that oil discovery (the rate of finding new reserves) peaked in the 1960s. In January 2004, Royal Dutch/Shell shocked markets by slashing its estimated oil and natural gas reserves by 20 percent, thereby reducing its reserve life by about one-quarter. Echoing these revelations, El Paso Gas announced in February 2004, a sharp reduction in its proven reserves of natural gas.

Depletion in some regions has not yet manifested itself in lower global production, primarily because swing producers in the Middle East, especially Saudi Arabia, Iran, and Qatar, have driven production higher than may be optimal in terms of maximizing total eventual recovery of oil in the ground. Consumers, too, prefer maximizing near-term production because it drives down price.

Political perturbations, rather than producer countries husbanding a resource that has scarcity value, are the major factors in current pricing. Nevertheless, depletion-driven, higher-priced energy may be in our future.

This brings us to the data supporting the connection between the availability of energy and population trends. The invention of multiple ways to harness the energy in

wood and coal launched the Industrial Revolution and rapid population growth. Fossil fuels accelerated these trends, with population expanding six-fold during the first half of the Oil Age (1859 to approximately 2000), according to Richard Heinberg. Energy economist Vaclav Smil observes that, "Population density increased substantially in countries with intensive agriculture only after the use of nitrogen fertilizer became common." After inventions in 1909, synthetic ammonia—made mostly from natural gas—began replacing natural sources of nitrogen and now accounts for essentially all inorganic

Jørgen Schytte/Still Pictures/Peter Arnold

Cairo tenement dwellers air their laundry. Approximately a third of Cairo's 16 million inhabitants live in slums.

nitrogen inputs to agriculture.

More specifically, the decades between 1950 and 1970 saw a near doubling of the per-capita use of industrial energy worldwide, from 1.03 to 2.04 kilowatts (kW). The rate of increase slowed in the following two decades, 1970 to 1990, when per-capita energy use increased from 2.04 to only 2.19 kW. With respect to oil alone, production and use peaked in the early 1970s at approximately 2.3 liters per person per day. By 2000, per-capita oil consumption had declined to approximately 1.7 liters per day.

Trends in world population growth roughly track the fluctuations in per-capita energy use. Population plotted on a semi-logarithmic scale yields a curve that

Haruyoshi Yamaguchi/REUTERS © 2002

A homeless man harvests aluminum cans for 78 U.S. cents per kilo (Osaka, Japan).

Caution: Children

Children are very costly in energetic terms, so it is to be expected that humans have evolved to avoid or undo reproductive mistakes. Cautious approaches to childbearing allow hoarding of resources for the most propitious opportunities, theoretically maximizing total reproductive success and giving the next generation a competitive edge.

My data suggest that persons who perceive improving conditions make expansive reproductive choices, relaxing prudential behavior and pleasurably anticipating large families. Today's young, however, largely expect narrowing opportunities. Anticipating difficulty in providing for children at a personally acceptable standard, they tend to be cautious about incurring family responsibilities. They avoid childbearing while single, delay marriage, and space children within marriage.

Choices may narrow rapidly if certain energy futures materialize. Rising energy prices may cause retrenchment in living standards. Food surpluses will disappear if growing national populations raise domestic demand, and price-induced reduction of petrochemical-based fertilizer and pesticides cut yields. Domestic demand will usually be satisfied before food is exported unless a severely indebted nation must sell to survive; export of food needed at home is a recipe for social unrest. But it is likely that, before these scenarios emerged, the native-born population and established residents would respond with marked reductions in their fertility rates. Barring mass immigration, population would begin to stabilize.

A public that opposes immigration and practices reproductive self-restraint has embarked already on a promising adaptation to petroleum depletion. Governments should support—rather than oppose, as they often do—both aspects of this adaptation. All else equal, a country with a stable or shrinking population is better positioned to cope with increasingly expensive energy. Worldwide, a future marked by declining energy use per capita may be the ultimate driver of population stabilization.

bends steeply upward, away from a straight line, from at least the beginning of the twentieth century until nearly 1970. That is, population size grew at *an accelerating rate so long as petroleum consumption per capita was also rising rapidly.* Between 1965 and 1970, world population growth slowed from its trajectory of 1.9 percent annually to the lower rate of 1.7 percent. By 2000, it had slowed to 1.4 percent annually. "Population momentum," the phenomenon that successively larger generations drives birth rates higher even when individual fertility is low, accounts for a lag between declining per-capita energy use and decline in the population growth rate.

Coal, nuclear, and renewable energy sources, combined with increasing efficiencies, may mitigate the effect of a plateau in oil and gas production. If not, the demographic effects of a no-growth or declining economy may be profound. Assuming some lag time, which could be relatively short, Colin Campbell comments that, "…the consequence of peak oil may be peak people."

Virginia Deane Abernethy *is professor of psychiatry emerita at Vanderbilt University and the author of* Population Politics *and* Population Pressure and Cultural Adjustment, *which was the earliest expression of her thesis and will be reissued in paperback in the spring of 2005.*

References and readings for each article are available at www.worldwatch.org/pubs/mag/.

ENVIRSCI 101   **Questions on Human Population Growth**

1. Based on the article by Steck (2007), about how many people were on Earth in 2007?

2. How does the human population in 2007 compare numerically to the population in 1800?

3. How has the world's population growth rate (as an annual percentage) changed since 1970?

4. What is replacement level fertility (i.e., as a number of births per woman over her lifetime) in most developed countries? Why is not this value exactly equal to 2.0?

5. Do the least developed countries have a different numerical value for replacement level fertility? Why? *(Note: The article does not explicitly say why. Please speculate.)*

6. Which industrialized (i.e., developed) country has the highest overall population growth rate, and how does this compare to most other industrialized countries. *(Slightly higher? What?)*

7. (Fig. 3) How do the average life expectancies at birth differ between the most and least developed countries? Why?

8. During the "demographic transition", both death rates and birth rates decrease from about 5% per year to about 1%. Which rate drops first?

9. What is the main reason that death rates have declined in most countries during the 20th century? (Fewer wars?) Did decreased in death rates have to await the arrival of "patient-directed medicine" (and what is *that*, anyway?)?

10. In rural areas of the least developed countries, what material incentives might parents have for rearing more than two children? *(Note: There are many more reasons than are offered in the article. Please speculate.)*

11. Is a larger or smaller fraction of a country's population likely to reside in urban settings at the end of the demographic transition compared to the beginning? Why?

12. How does the balance of costs versus benefits of having more than two children per family change during the demographic transition? Which benefits change? How? Which costs?

13. What rights and services usually develop during the demographic transition that have fertility-lowering effects?

14. Does the transmission of knowledge regarding "modern" lifestyles appear to influence reproductive choices in premodern communities? How might this work?

15. Beginning at the bottom of p. 6, Steck (2007) list seven pro-natalist arguments. Please attack or defend one or more of these arguments.

16. (Abernethy, 2004) Did Thomas Malthus really believe that the only mechanisms that could limit the size of the human population were unpleasant things like famine, war, and pestilence? Explain.

17. What does Abernethy's **Fertility Opportunity Hypothesis** say about the relationship between *perceived* deprivation and fertility?

18. Who would be more likely to perceive themselves as living in a period of deprivation: 1, a farming couple in a rural village lacking TVs, radios, newspapers and other means for learning much about the outside world; or 2, a couple living in a former Soviet block country in the 1990s during the socioeconomic upheavals that followed the collapse of communism? Which couple is more likely to have more than two children?

19. How can people lacking access to modern contraceptive methods reduce their fertility? [*Ideas are offered in the second column of p. 26 of Abernethy (2004) and in the third paragraph of p. 4 of Steck (2007).*]

20. (Abernethy, p. 26, col. 3, paragr. 3) Most demographers think that explosive population growth occurs in developing countries early in the demographic transition almost entirely because more developed countries introduce death-rate-reducing technologies. Does Abernethy think this is the only effect the more developed countries have had?

21. (Abernethy, p. 27) How does the history of Rwanda between 1950 and 1993 support the Fertility Opportunity Hypothesis?

22. Between 1970 and 1990, fertility rates in northeastern Brazil dropped from 7 to 3.7 births/woman. Did this happen because that region of Brazil made major progress through the demographic transition, so that most people became more affluent?

23. Do the histories of Egypt and Morocco lend more support to the Fertility Opportunity Hypothesis or to the traditional demographic view that and increase in affluence is needed to elicit and decrease in fertility?

24. Among the nations known as the "Asian tigers", did fertility decrease more during economic boom periods or during the economic bust of the late 1990s?

25. Abernethy (2004) defends the view that rising energy (esp. oil) costs will depress fertility in many countries. How might this work? In what ways could rising oil and gas prices increase potential parents' sense of "deprivation"?

26. Could the Fertility-Opportunity effect and the affluence-as-contraceptive effect work most strongly across different time frames? Is one more of a short-term effect and the other long-term? How might this work?

27. Some of Dr. Abernethy's critics have argued that her Fertility Opportunity Hypothesis would predict that the efforts of developed countries to relieve suffering in the least developed countries will backfire by triggering a increase in fertility. Please offer an example or two of a situation in which this might happen? Does this mean we should withhold food aid during famines or refuse to share technology with poor countries?

Two Brief Articles on Problems Faced by Small Populations

Safety in numbers

(*New Scientist* 03 February 2001)

Adrian Barnett

Animals can die out even when there's plenty of food and space. Adrian Barnett finds out why conserving species involves more than counting two by two.

WALLACE CRAIG cupped the lifeless feathery bundle in his hands and sighed. Glancing at his watch he noted the time: 1:00 pm. The date was 1 September 1914, and Martha the passenger pigeon had just expired. With her went an entire species.

It was the most unlikely extinction. In the early 18th century flocks of migrating passenger pigeons had darkened the skies above eastern North America, taking three days to pass by. Hunters simply pointed a gun upwards, fired, and then got out the way as the pigeons tumbled to Earth. When the birds stopped to roost, trees broke under their combined weight. With an estimated population of somewhere between 3 and 5 billion, the passenger pigeon was the most abundant bird that ever lived. Yet by the late 1890s the species was almost extinct. A few birds found their way to zoos, but they languished in captivity and refused to breed.

It was a result that perplexed Craig and his contemporaries, and today's conservationists often face a similar problem. It isn't just that living in a zoo can ruin an animal's sex life. When wild species experience a population crash they too can go into free fall, even though you would think that by removing the pressure of overcrowding, the survivors would flourish. Now conservationists are beginning to realise that under-crowding itself can help drive species to extinction. It's a counterintuitive idea, but it's not a new

one: the consequences of low population density were first studied more than half a century ago by American biologist Warder Allee.

For decades his ideas were largely forgotten, but now an awareness of these "Allee effects" looks set to transform conservation practices. "They alter our perception about the risks facing populations that have declined markedly, even if they are not numerically tiny," says Georgina Mace from the Institute of Zoology in London.

"Allee effects centre on the observation that some species find it very difficult to breed successfully once the population falls below a certain number or density," says Franck Courchamp of the University of Paris-Sud. "It used to be thought that such populations would simply rebound, but clearly this isn't always the case," adds Philip Stephens from the University of East Anglia. And as Allee pointed out, there are various reasons why.

For some species, such as blue whales, it is simply that with only a few, solitary individuals remaining, finding a mate can prove extremely difficult. It's a little more complicated for New Zealand's giant flightless parrot, the kakapo, where dwindling numbers mean insufficient males coming together at breeding time. Male kakapos gather at leks and the females are attracted by their multiple calls-a bit of a problem when the world population is down to 54 dispersed individuals. A similar fate could await other species that use leks, such as the European black grouse and South America's cock-of-the-rock.

Perhaps the commonest Allee effect occurs in species that congregate to protect themselves against predators. Animals such as flamingos and penguins just won't get into breeding mood unless they are surrounded by many other mating individuals. In such species, natural selection favours animals that synchronise their breeding because their offspring are more likely to survive the vulnerable early weeks if there are plenty of other young animals around for potential predators to pick off. "This may not be a problem for a species that is usually abundant," says Bill Sutherland from the University of East Anglia, "but can become important once it becomes rare or once people are trying to breed it in captivity." In some species, a behaviour that probably evolved as a way of swamping potential predators, seems to have developed into a near-unbreakable psychological dependence.

"But Allee effects can be more subtle and complex in group-living species," says Courchamp, who was until recently, part of a team from Cambridge University studying the African hunting dog, *Lycaon pictus*. Once numerous and widespread, the hunting dog is now Africa's most endangered large carnivore. "Declines of up to 30 per cent occurred even in protected areas where other previously persecuted species like spotted hyena were increasing," says David Macdonald, director of the Wildlife Conservation Research Unit at Oxford University. The reason for this was a real puzzle.

The Cambridge team was led by Tim Clutton-Brock who had previously studied Kalahari meerkats. Meerkats are cooperative breeders, which rely on helpers to raise their pups, and Clutton-Brock had found that small groups were far more likely to die out than large ones. Could the peculiar social system of *Lycaon* make it similarly vulnerable? Digging around in the literature, Courchamp found a treasure trove of studies showing how reduced population density could adversely affect the rate of population growth of many species. "It was all being totally ignored," he says. The team started to

suspect that Allee effects might be to blame for the hunting dog's failure to flourish.

African hunting dogs have a rather odd social life. When the young reach reproductive age they leave the pack with a group of up to six other individuals of the same sex. A new pack is formed when they meet a group of the opposite sex. One pair becomes dominant and they alone breed, while the rest hunt and look after the puppies. The researchers wondered whether there was a minimum pack size, below which survival was difficult. Using a mathematical model and the field observations of other researchers including Scott Creel from the University of Montana and Greg Rasmussen from Oxford University, they found there was: three or four adults plus the breeding pair. "Smaller packs find it hard because helpers are needed for cooperative hunting and to defend kills from lions and hyenas," says Courchamp. The problem is that these same adults must also care for the pups. "And smaller packs will send off smaller cohorts to colonise new areas," says Clutton-Brock, so the problem continues to the next generation.

"The *Lycaon* study was the first time an Allee effect has been fully demonstrated, and it could have major implications for the conservation of other cooperative breeders," says Clutton-Brock. Animals that have no alternative but to rely on one another for breeding success are most at risk from this particular form of under-crowding. The effect will be strongest in species such as the naked mole-rat, white-winged chough and social insects, predicts Clutton-Brock. Less at risk are animals that help each other to raise young but do not rely so heavily on such cooperation, including wolves, lions and marmosets. Even so, this effect may explain the slow recovery of the Ethiopian wolf following a rabies epidemic that wiped out much of the population between 1988 and 1992.

Allee effects are not confined to purely social species or, indeed, animals. Those that simply aggregate may also be vulnerable. For example, hemlock trees outcompete other species by producing acids which they pump into the surrounding soil to raise its water content and drown out competitors. The more hemlocks in any patch of forest, the more dramatic the effect. So despite the fact that the densely packed trees are competing for sunlight and nutrients, hemlocks grow faster in a crowd than when they are thinly spread.

Indeed, researchers including Clutton-Brock have come to the conclusion that Allee effects are widespread. "Many species may show Allee effects when populations reach extremely low densities," he says. "However, they probably occur at a wide range of densities in cooperative species where breeding success and survival increase with group size." And the implications are far from academic.

Take the strongly schooling fish that make up many of the world's most important commercial fisheries (New Scientist, 27 January, p 16). North Atlantic herring stocks, for example, have failed to recover despite a 25-year fishing ban, and the annual haul of Peruvian anchovies has plummeted from 11 million tonnes in the late 1960s to less than 100,000 tonnes today. Many fisheries biologists believe that once numbers of these sorts of fish fall below a certain point, predators become a significant force. Where in the past they would have merely nibbled at the edges of vast shoals, they may now be doing enough damage to check the population's expansion.

The effects of under-crowding can also threaten attempts to reintroduce endangered species into the wild. Australian biologists trying to establish a wild population of rare marsupials called bush-tailed phascogales, *Phascogale tapoatafa*, for example, first tried releasing the males and females together. But this strategy failed because the animals dispersed and then the males couldn't find the females. Once the team realised what was happening they were able to minimise this effect by simply releasing the females first and allowing them to establish and mark their territories before introducing the males, who could then track them down.

Allee effects could also have major implications for the success of biological controls. Some 65 per cent of attempts to control insects and 41 per cent of agents freed to destroy weeds never became effectively established. "Most such releases flop," says Rob Freckleton from Oxford University. He believes there's good evidence that Allee effects underlie many of these failures, and points to the gorse thrip as an example. The effectiveness of this tiny insect against invading gorse plants increases in proportion to the number of thrips initially released. "Numbers used in releases are often simply too small for populations to breed," says Freckleton. "This not only wastes a lot of money and effort, it also turns people away from control agents that might have been successful if only the right release procedure had been used."

If Allee effects are so far-reaching, why did the idea languish for 50 years? "I honestly don't know," says Courchamp, pointing out that there have always been scattered papers on the subject. Stephens points out that Allee was way ahead of his time. "The major population dynamic debates in Allee's day were about top-end regulation of populations-what prevented them from growing indefinitely, or cycling irregularly," says Stephens. "There was little concern about extinction back then, or the problems of small populations. Interest in low-end population dynamics was very limited. So the Allee effect simply never caught on at the time."

Today concern about the biodiversity crisis has changed all that, putting Allee effects at the cutting edge of conservation concepts. Their revival also reflects the trend for thinking about conservation in behavioural biology terms. "This work on Allee effects is another illustration of the importance of individual behaviour-especially social behaviour-in population processes," Macdonald says. "This is vital for conservation planning. Too often people treat populations as if individuals were merely numbers, whereas the reality is that they are behaviourally complex, and management must take account of that."

But bringing this approach to mainstream conservation isn't going to be plain sailing. So far, there have been very few field studies done with Allee effects in mind, and some conservation biologists feel the approach is irrelevant to their work. "There is, for example, a lingering perception that the Allee effect is a phenomenon only of very small populations and thus of limited importance to conservationists," says Stephens. He believes that Allee effects can determine the growth and dynamics of any population, small or large.

To most people who have embraced the study of Allee effects, it is the potential impact on practical conservation that fuels their research. Their only regret is that the importance of Allee's work was not recognised from the start. "The threats of over-exploitation, habitat fragmentation and so on might have been focused on sooner," says Stephens. "Conservation science might have developed earlier, with a fully developed, unifying theory to hand."

Even if that had happened it would have been too late for Martha and the last few passenger pigeons.

Further reading:

Consequences of the Allee effect for behaviour, ecology and conservation by Philip Stephens and William Sutherland, *Trends in Ecology and Evolution*, vol 14, p 401 (1999)

Inverse density dependence and the Allee effect by Franck Courchamp and others, *Trends in Ecology and Evolution*, vol 14, p 405 (1999)

Vertebrate mating systems, Allee effects and conservation by Philip Stephens and William Sutherland in Vertebrate Mating System (Word Scientific Publishing, 2000, London)

Adrian Barnett is a freelance writer and ecologist based at the University of Surrey Roehampton in London

---

Linking Forest Fragments Boosts Red Squirrel's Diminishing Genetic Diversity
(*Scientific American* 21 September 2001)

Kate Wong

To maintain healthy levels of genetic diversity, animal populations need to remain sufficiently large. As habitats become fragmented, however, so too do the resident populations, which can result in a loss of genetic variation. That, in turn, puts these populations at risk of extinction. But if the habitat fragments are linked by corridors, or "stepping stone" patches, they can serve as a single large habitat.

A new study reveals dramatic evidence of this fact. Reporting today in the journal *Science*, researchers describe how habitat defragmentation boosted genetic diversity in British red squirrel populations. The authors note that the findings could have important implications for conservation management of species that occupy fragmented landscapes.

Though their numbers have plummeted elsewhere, red squirrels remain relatively abundant in northern England and southern Scotland, inhabiting a patchwork of forest fragments. To assess how the recent planting of a large new forest linking the patches in the two regions might have impacted the local squirrel populations, Marie L. Hale of the University of Newcastle and colleagues studied genetic markers in 102 dried red-squirrel skins collected in Britain over the past century. Squirrels from the Cumbria region held the key, reflecting an increase in genetic diversity in the 1980s. That surge, it turns out, corresponds to the timing of the maturation of a new forest, which the squirrels apparently used to migrate between western and northern forest fragments. Indeed, the researchers report, the landscape defragmentation led to "substantial genetic mixing of Scottish and Cumbrian genes in squirrel populations up to 100 kilometers away from the site of the new forest."

"These findings suggest that where a network of stepping stones is available within a critical dispersal distance, gene flow can be very rapid through highly fragmented landscapes," the authors conclude. Furthermore, they observe, the study indicates that human-made alterations affecting the connectivity of a landscape can bring about changes in genetic makeup "not only in the area of habitat change but in the populations hundreds of kilometers from the site of habitat change.

Questions from the Allee-effect article

1. What biologically note-worthy death occurred on Sept. 1st 1914?

2. How would you describe in general terms what the article calls an "Allee Effect"?

3. Do all species that manifest an Allee effect at low population densities have problems reproducing because of the same fundamental reason? Give an example of one cause of an Allee effect in a particular critter.

4. Why do blue whales have problems reproducing now?

5. What is the reproductive problem faced by lek breeding species like European black grouse or New Zealand's kakapo's at low population densities?

6. Why might Peruvian anchovies or Atlantic herring be suffering an Allee effect that prevents their populations from rapidly rebounding from the low numbers to which over-fishing reduced them?

7. I understand that many fish and birds join in schools and flocks to swamp predators and improve each individual's odds of survival. But, why would it work as a predator avoidance scheme for penguins to cluster into large colonies and breed all at the same time?

8. The article is oddly silent about an obvious evolutionary conundrum. If three or four pairs of penguins get lost from the rest of their colony and find themselves isolated as a tiny group on an otherwise suitable stretch of coastline, how could it be selectively advantageous for them to refrain from breeding?

9. African hunting dogs and North American coyotes are both canids that run in packs. How does the way African hunting dogs reproduce differ from the way that you think coyotes are likely to reproduce?

10. Why does the cooperative breeding strategy of African Hunting dogs put them at high risk of reproductive failure if their populations go into a decline?

11. Why do hemlock trees grow better in a crowd, despite the fierceness with which they compete with one another then they grow if scattered individually throughout a forest.

12. What were the "wrong" way and the "right" way to reintroduce the bush-tailed phascogales into the former habitat in the wilds of Australia, and what made the "right" way more successful?

13. The conservation biologists tried to reintroduce a modest number a phascogales to an habitat devoid of them. Would the same mechanism that caused the "wrong" reintroduction technique to fail have produced an Allee effect in a population of phascogales that was being slowly reduced in density, e.g., by hunting or collecting for pets?

There's a lot of pontificating at the end of the first article from which I could derive no decent questions for discussion.

Questions from the red-squirrel article

14. Why is it a bad idea for brothers to mate with their sisters? Why do societies (usually - not for ancient Egyptian royals) have social taboos against incest so powerful that Oedipus gouged his eyes out when he discovered he had married his mother?

15. Many zoologists think there is genetic evidence that cheetahs suffered a catastrophic population collapse in the not too distant past that reduced their numbers to perhaps as few as one or two dozens individuals. What effect must this have had on their genetic variability, and, in consequence, do you think zoos have an easier time breeding cheetahs or lions in captivity?

16. Why are populations of red squirrels thriving in northern England and southern Scotland, "though their numbers have plummeted elsewhere"?

17. Exactly what was the evidence on which the squirrel researchers based their claims that connecting the formerly isolated patches of squirrel inhabited forest really had increased the genetic diversity of the red squirrels? *(Hint: DNA from pelts.)*

The following article, while showing its age, still compactly summarizes the major benefits of tropical rainforests and the forces that lead to their destruction. Students desiring a (longer but) more up-to-date discussion of the state of the world's rainforests are referred to the extensive set of articles accessible through the following URL: http://rainforests.mongabay.com/

The use of information from this website would be completely appropriate in formulating answers to some of the discussion questions at the end of the article below.

PLAYING WITH FIRE

By Eugene Linden

The skies over western Brazil will soon be dark both day and night. Dark from the smoke of thousands of fires, as farmers and cattle ranchers engage in their annual rite of destruction: clearing land for crops and livestock by burning the rainforests of the Amazon. Unusually heavy rains have slowed down the burning this year, but the dry season could come at any time, and then the fires will reach a peak. Last year the smoke grew so thick that Porto Velho, the capital of the state of Rondonia, was forced to close its airport for days at a time. An estimated 12,350 square miles of Brazilian rainforest—an area larger than Belgium—was reduced to ashes. Anticipating another conflagration this year, scientists, environmentalists, and TV crews have journeyed to Porto Velho to marvel and despair at the immolation of these ancient forests.

After years of inattention, the whole world has awakened at last to how much is at stake in the Amazon. It has become the front line in the battle to rescue earth's endangered environment from humanity's destructive ways. "Save the rainforest," long a rallying cry for conservationists, is now being heard from politicians, pundits, and rock stars. The movement has sparked a confrontation between rich industrial nations, which are fresh converts to the environmental cause, and the poorer nations of the Third World, which view outside interference as an assault on their sovereignty.

Some of the harshest criticism is aimed at Brazil. The largest South American country embraces about half the Amazon basin and, in the eyes of critics, has shown a reckless penchant for squandering resources that matter to all mankind. Government leaders around the world are calling on Brazil to stop the burning. Two delegations from the U.S. Congress, which included Sen. Albert Gore, Jr., of Tennessee and Sen. John Chafee of Rhode Island, traveled to the Amazon earlier this year [1989] to see the plight of the rainforest firsthand. Says Gore: "The devastation is just unbelievable. It's one of the greatest tragedies of all history."

The vast region of unbroken green that

It's dangerous to say the forest will disappear by a particular year, but unless things change, the forest will disappear.

surrounds the Amazon River and its tributaries has been under assault by settlers and developers for 400 years. Time and again, the forest has defied predictions that it was doomed. But now the danger is more real and imminent than ever before, as loggers level trees, dams flood vast tracts of land, and gold miners poison rivers with mercury. In Peru the forests are being cleared to grow coca for cocaine production. "It's dangerous to say the forest will disappear by a particular year," says Philip Fearnside of Brazil's National Institute for Research in the Amazon, "but unless things change, the forest *will* disappear."

That would be more than a South American disaster. It would be an incalculable catastrophe for the entire planet. Moist tropical forests are distinguished by their canopies of interlocking leaves and branches that shelter creatures below from sun and wind, and by their incredible variety of animal and plant life. If the forests vanish, so will more than 1 million species—a significant part of earth's biological diversity and genetic heritage. Moreover, the burning of the Amazon could have dramatic effects on global weather patterns—for example, heightening the warming trend that may result from the greenhouse effect. "The Amazon is a library for life sciences, the world's greatest pharmaceutical laboratory, and a flywheel of climate," says Thomas Lovejoy of the Smithsonian Institution. "It's a matter of global destiny."

To Brazilians, such pressure amounts to unjustified foreign meddling and a blatant effort by the industrial nations to preserve their economic supremacy at the expense of the developing world. Brazilian President Jose Sarney has denounced the criticism of his country as "unjust, defamatory, cruel, and indecent." How can Brazil be expected to control its economic development, he asks, when it is staggering under a $111 billion foreign debt load? By what right does the United States, which spews out more pollutants than any other nation, lecture poor countries like Brazil on their responsibilities to mankind?

Yet Sarney is caught between conflicting, and sometimes violent, forces within his nation. On one side are the settlers and developers, often backed by corrupt politicians, who are razing the forests to lay claim to the land. On the other are hundreds of fledgling conservation groups, along with the Indian tribes and rubber tappers whose way of life will be destroyed if the forests disappear. The clash has already produced the world's most celebrated environmental martyr, Chico Mendes, a leader of the rubber tappers who was murdered for trying to stand in the way of ranchers.

The passions behind the fight are easy to understand for anyone who has seen the almost unimaginable sweep of the Amazon basin. The river and forest system covers 2.7 million square miles (almost 90 percent of the area of the contiguous United States) and stretches into eight countries beside Brazil, including Venezuela to the north, Peru to the west, and Bolivia to the south. An adventurous monkey could climb into the jungle canopy in the foothills of the Andes and swing through 2,000 miles of continuous 200-foot-high forest before reaching the Atlantic coast. The river itself,

:ed by more than 1,000 tributaries, meanders for 4,000 miles, a length second only to the Nile's 4,100 miles. No other river compares in volume: Every hour the Amazon delivers an average of 170 billion gallons of water to the Atlantic—60 times the flow of the Nile. Even 1,000 miles upriver, it is often impossible to see from one side of the Amazon to the other.

The Living Jungle

The jungle is so dense and teeming that all the biologists on earth could not fully describe its life forms. A 1982 U.S. National Academy of Sciences report estimated that a typical 4-square-mile patch of rainforest may contain 750 species of trees, 125 kinds of mammals, 400 types of birds, 100 kinds of reptiles, and 60 amphibians. Each type of tree may support more than 400 insect species. In many cases the plants and animals assume Amazonian proportions: lily pads that are 3 feet or more across, butterflies with 8-inch wing spans, and a fish called the pirarucu, which can grow to more than 7 feet long. Amid the vast assortment of jungle life, creatures command every trick in nature's book to fool or repel predators, attract mates, and grab food. Caterpillars masquerade as snakes, plants exude the smell of rotting meat to attract flies as pollinators, and trees rely on fish to distribute their seeds when the rivers flood.

But the diversity of the Amazon is more than just good material for TV specials. The rainforest is a virtually untapped storehouse of evolutionary achievement that will prove increasingly valuable to mankind as it yields its secrets. Agronomists see the forest as a cornucopia of undiscovered food sources, and chemists scour the flora and fauna for compounds with seemingly magical properties. For instance, the piquia tree produces a compound that appears to be toxic to leaf-cutter ants, which cause millions of dollars of damage each year to South American agriculture. Such chemicals promise attractive alternatives to dangerous synthetic pesticides. Other jungle chemicals have already led to new treatments for hypertension and some forms of cancer. The lessons encoded in the genes of the Amazon's plants and animals may ultimately hold the key to solving a wide range of human problems.

Scientists are concerned that the destruction of the Amazon could lead to climatic chaos. Because of the huge volume of clouds it generates, the Amazon system plays a major role in the way the sun's heat is distributed around the globe. Any disturbance of this process could produce far-reaching, unpredictable effects. Moreover, the Amazon region stores at least 75 billion tons of carbon in its trees, which when burned spew carbon dioxide (CO_2) into the atmosphere. Since the air is already dangerously overburdened by carbon dioxide from the cars and factories of industrial nations, the torching of the Amazon could magnify the greenhouse effect—the trapping of heat by atmospheric CO_2. No one knows just what impact the buildup of CO_2 will have, but some scientists fear that the globe will begin to warm up, bringing on wrenching climatic changes.

A Popular Cause

As the potential consequences of rainforest destruction became more widely known, saving the Amazon became the cause of 1989. In New York City, Madonna helped organize a benefit concert called Don't Bungle the Jungle, which also featured the B–52s and the Grateful Dead's Bob Weir. Xapuri, the remote town where Mendes lived and died, has been besieged by journalists, agents, and pilgrims. Robert Redford, David Puttnam, and other prominent moviemakers have sought the rights to film the Mendes story.

In the face of pressure from abroad and complaints from environmentalists at home, Brazil has grudgingly begun to respond. In April [1989], only a few months after denouncing the environmental movement as a foreign plot to seize the forests, the Sarney administration announced a hastily patched-together conservation package dubbed Our Nature. Much of the language was ambiguous, but the program contained promising provisions, such as the temporary suspension of tax incentives that spur the most wasteful forest exploitation. Says Celio Valle, director of ecosystems at the government's newly created environmental agency: "Before, we used to consider Brazilian environmental groups as the enemy, but now we consider them allies." Amazonian development may become a significant issue in this fall's [1989] presidential campaign. Fernando Collor de Mello, a member of the conservative National Reconstruction Party and a leading candidate to succeed Sarney, has said he believes in preserving the forests, though critics doubt his sincerity.

Many Brazilians still believe the Amazon is indestructible—a green monster so huge and vital that it could not possibly disappear. Asked about a controversial hydroelectric project that might flood an area as large as Britain, a Brazilian engineering consultant said, "Yes, that's a big area, but in terms of the Amazon it's small." Maintained Sarney recently: "It's not easy to destroy a rainforest. There are recuperative powers at work."

Yet the rainforest is deceptively fragile. Left to itself, it is an almost self-sustaining ecosystem that thrives indefinitely. But it does not adapt well to human invasions and resists being turned into farmland or ranchland. Most settlers find that the lush promise of the Amazon is an illusion that vanishes when grasped.

The forest functions like a delicately balanced organism that recycles most of its nutrients and much of its moisture. Wisps of steam float from the top of the endless palette of green as water evaporates off the upper leaves, cooling the trees as they collect the intense sunlight. Air currents over the forest gather this evaporation into clouds, which return the moisture to th system in torrential rains. Dead anima and vegetation decompose quickly, and the resulting nutrients move rapidly from the soil back to growing plants. The forest is such an efficient recycler that virtually no decaying matter seeps into the region's rivers.

But when stripped of its trees, the land becomes inhospitable. Most of the Amazon's soil is nutrient-poor and ill-suited to agriculture. The rainforest has an uncanny capacity to flourish in soils that elsewhere would not even support weeds.

Dreamers and Schemers

Throughout history, would-be pioneers and developers have discovered just h(unreceptive the Amazon can be. Henry Ford tried twice to carve rubber empires out of the rainforest in the 1920s and 1930s. But when the protective canopy was cut down, the rubber trees withered under the assault of sun, rain, and pests. In 1967 Daniel Ludwig, an American billionaire, launched a rashly ambitious project to clear 2.5 million acres of forest and plant gmelina trees for their timber. He figured that the imported species would not be susceptible to Brazil's pests. Ludwig was wrong, and as his trees died off, he bailed out of the project in 1982.

The Brazilian government, meanwhile, came up with development schemes of its own. In the early 1970s the country built the Trans-Amazon Highway, a system of roads that run west from the coastal city of Recife toward the Peruvian border. The idea was to prompt a land rush similar to the pioneering of the American West. To encourage settlers to brave the jungle, the government offered transportation and other incentives, allowing them to claim land that they had "improved" by cutting down the trees.

But for most of the roughly 8,000 families that heeded the government's call between 1970 and 1974, the dream turned into a bitter disappointment. The soil, unlike the rich sod in the western United States, was so poor that crop yields began to deteriorate badly after three or four years. Most settlers eventually gave up and left.

Yet the failed dreams of yesterday have not discouraged Brazil from conjuring up more grand visions for today. The country has continued to build roads, dams, and settlements, often with funding and technical advice from the World Bank, the European community, and Japan. Two of the largest—and, to the rainforest, most threatening—projects are Grande Carajas, a giant development program that includes a major mining complex, and Polonoroeste, a highway-and-settlement scheme.

The $3.5 billion, 324,000-square-mile Grande Carajas Program, located in the eastern Amazon, seeks to exploit Brazil's mineral deposits, perhaps the world's largest, which include iron ore, manganese, bauxite, copper, and nickel. The principal iron-ore mine began production in 1985, and its operation has little impact on the forest. The problem, however, is the smelters that convert the ore into pig iron. They are powered by charcoal, and the cheapest way to obtain it is by chopping down the surrounding forests and burning the trees. Environmentalists fear that Grande Carajas will repeat the dismal experience of the state of Minas Gerais in southeastern Brazil, where pig-iron production consumed nearly two-thirds of the state's forests.

In the other huge project, Polonoroeste, the government is trying to develop

WHAT YOU CAN DO

The Nature Conservancy has formed an "Adopt-an-Acre Program" that enables individuals to buy and protect specific areas of threatened rainforest. For $30, you can adopt one acre of tropical land. In return, you'll receive an honorary land deed, information about the protected area, and semiannual letters from a local conservationist involved in managing the area. For more info, contact the Nature Conservancy, 1815 N. Lynn St., Arlington, VA 22209 or call (800) 872-1899.

the sprawling western state of Rondonia. The program, backed by subsidies and built around a highway through the state called BR–364, was designed to relieve population pressures in southern Brazil. But Polonoroeste has made Rondonia the area where rainforest destruction is most rapid, and the focal point of the fight to save the Amazon.

The results of the development have been chaotic and in some cases tragic. Machadinho, for instance, was supposed to be a model settlement village with gravel roads, schools, and health clinics. But when a surge of migrants traveled down BR–364 to Machadinho in 1985, orderly development became a pell-mell land grab. Settlers encountered the familiar scourges of the rainforest: poor soil and inescapable mosquito-borne disease. Decio Fujizaki, a settler who came west four years ago, has just contracted malaria for the umpteenth time. Says he: "I always wanted my own plot of land. If only it wasn't for this wretched disease."

Instead of model settlements, the Polonoroeste project has produced impoverished itinerants. Settlers grow rice, corn, coffee, and manioc for a few years, until the meager soil is exhausted, then move deeper into the forest to clear new land. The farming and burning thus become a perpetual cycle of depredation. Thousands of pioneers give up on farming altogether and migrate to the Amazon's new cities to find work. For many, the net effect of the attempt to colonize Rondonia has been a shift from urban slums to Amazonian slums. Says Donald Sawyer, a demographer from the University of Minas Gerais: "The word is out that living on a 125-acre plot in the jungle is not that good."

The abandoned fields wind up in the hands of ranchers and speculators who have access to capital. Thanks to tax breaks and subsidies, these groups can often profit from the land even when their operations lose money. According to Roberto Alusio Paranhos do Rio Branco, president of the Business Association of the Amazon, nobody would farm Rondonia without government incentives and price supports for cocoa and other crops.

Rondonia's native Indians have fared worse than the settlers. Swept over by the land rush, one tribe, the Nambiquara, lost half its population to violent clashes with the immigrants and newly introduced diseases like measles. Jason Clay, director of research for Cultural Survival, an advocacy organization for the Indians, says that when the Nambiquara were relocated as part of Polonoroeste, the move severed an intimate connection, forged over generations, to the foods and medicines of their traditional lands. That deprived them of their livelihood and posterity of a wealth of information about the riches of the forest. Says Clay: "Move a hunter-gatherer tribe 50 miles, and they'll starve to death."

Forest Loss Continues

Amid the suffering of natives and settlers, the one constant is that deforestation continues. Since 1980 the percentage of Rondonia covered by virgin forest has dropped from 97 percent to 80 percent. Says Jim LaFleur, an agricultural consultant with 13 years' experience working on colonization projects in Rondonia: "When I fly over the state, it's shocking. It's like watching a sheet of paper burn from the inside out."

A similar debacle could occur in the western state of Acre. It is still virtually pristine, having lost only 4 percent of its forests, but the rate of deforestation is increasing sharply as cattle ranchers expand their domain. Development in Acre has sparked a series of bloody confrontations between ranchers and rubber tappers, who want to preserve the forests so they can save their traditional livelihood of harvesting latex and Brazil nuts. It was this conflict that killed Mendes.

This courageous leader did not set out to save the Amazon but to improve the lot of rubber tappers, or *seringueiros*. He and his men would try to dissuade peasants from clearing land. The ranchers were eager to get rid of him, but he survived one assassination attempt after another. The conflict finally came to a head last year, when Mendes confronted a rancher named Darli Alves da Silva, who wanted to cross land claimed by rubber tappers to cut an adjacent 300-acre plot. After Mendes and a group of 200 seringueiros peacefully turned back the rancher and 40 peons, death threats against him grew more frequent. In December he was killed with a shotgun as he stepped out of his doorway. Alves and two of his sons were convicted of the murder but have appealed the verdict.

Mendes became a hero to environmentalists not only because he fought and died to stop deforestation but also because of the way of life he was defending. The rubber tappers are living proof that poor Brazilians can profit from the forest without destroying it. According to Stephan Schwartzman of the Environmental Defense Fund, seringueiros achieve a higher standard of living by harvesting the forest's bounty than do farmers who cut the forest and plant crops.

One of Mendes' most important achievements was to help convince the Inter-American Development Bank to suspend funding temporarily for further paving of BR–364 between Rondonia and Acre. But the Brazilian government is again seeking the $350 million needed to complete the road all the way to Peru, a prospect that alarms environmentalists. "One lesson we have learned in the Amazon is that when you improve a road, you unleash uncontrolled development on the rainforest," says John Browder, a specialist on Rondonia's deforestation from Virginia Polytechnic Institute.

Among other things, environmentalists fear that completion of the road will provide entree for Japanese trading companies that covet the Amazon's vast timber resources. Acre's governor, however, argues that the road is needed to end the state's isolation and claims that the state will not repeat the mistakes of Rondonia.

The debate over the Acre road places environmentalists in an uncomfortable position, essentially telling Brazilians that they cannot be trusted with their own development. Raimundo Marques da Silva, a retired public servant who helped build Acre's original dirt highway, asks, "How would Americans feel if years ago we had told them they could not build a road from New York to California because it would destroy their forests?"

Still, some Brazilians do accept that the outside world has a legitimate interest in the Amazon. Jose Lutzenberger, an outspoken environmentalist, notes that the Brazilians trying to develop the rainforest are themselves outsiders to the area. "This talk of 'We can do with our land what we want' is not true," he says. "If you set your house on fire it will threaten the homes of your neighbors."

If the rainforest disappears, the process will begin at its edges, in places such as Acre and Rondonia. While the Amazon forest as a whole generates roughly half of its own moisture, the percentage is much higher in these western states, far from the Atlantic. This means that deforestation is likely to have a more dramatic impact on the climate in the west than it would in the east. "Imagine the effects of a dry season extended by two months," says Fearnside, of Brazil's National Institute for Research in the Amazon. The process of deforestation could become self-perpetuating as heat, drying, and wind cause the trees to die on their own.

Exploring Alternatives

This does not have to happen. A dramatic drop in Brazil's birth rate promises to reduce future pressures to cut the forests, and experts believe the country could halt much of the deforestation with a few actions. By removing the remaining subsidies and incentives for clearing land, Brazil could both save money and slow the speculation that destroys the forests. Many environmentalists prefer this approach to the enactment of new laws. Brazilians have developed a genius, which they call *jeito*, for getting around laws, and many sound environmental statutes on the books are ignored.

The government could also stop some of the more wasteful projects it is currently planning. Part of the problem in the Amazon has been ill-conceived plans for development that destroy forests and drive the country deeper into debt. Most hydroelectric dams, for example, have proved unsuitable in the region. The Balbina Dam, which was completed in 1987 and began operating early this year [1989], flooded a huge area at great cost to produce relatively little power. It killed trees, poisoned fish, and provided breeding grounds for billions of malarial mosquitoes. Despite this experience, the government plans to build scores of additional dams.

Fabio Feldmann, the leading environmentalist in the Brazilian congress, alleges that much of the momentum behind the dam projects and other large public works derives from an extremely lucrative relationship between the major contractors and politicians. A dam may not have to make all that much sense if it generates sufficient *commissao* (commissions) for the right people.

If the burning of the forests goes on much longer, the damage may become irreversible.

Perhaps the best hope for the forests' survival is the growing recognition that they are more valuable when left standing than when cut. Charles Peters of the Institute of Economic Botany at the New York Botanical Garden recently published the results of a three-year study that calculate the market value of rubber and exotic products like the aguaje palm fruit that can be harvested from the Amazonian jungle. The study, which appeared in the British journal *Nature*, asserts that over time, selling these projects could yield more than twice the income of either cattle ranching or lumbering.

But if the burning of the forests goes on much longer, the damage may become irreversible. Long before the great rainforests are destroyed altogether, the impact of deforestation on climate could dramatically change the character of the area, lead to mass extinctions of plant and animal species, and leave Brazil's poor to endure even greater misery than they do now. The people of the rest of the world, no less than the Brazilians, need the Amazon as a functioning system, and in the end, this is more important than the issue of who owns the forest. The Amazon may run through South America, but the responsibility for saving the rainforests, as well as the reward for succeeding, belongs to everyone.

Discussion Questions

1. The author states that the movement to save the rainforests "sparked a confrontation between rich industrial nations... and the poorer nations of the Third World..." *(p. 129)*. What events or debates can you think of that are current examples of this type of confrontation? What specific positions do the two sides hold?

2. What are the specific economic activities which result in the destruction of rainforest trees? *(approximately 5 are listed in the article)*.

3. What was the initial response of the (former) president of Brazil Jose Sarney to criticism of Brazil's role in rainforest destruction? *(p. 130.)* What is your reaction to this argument?

4. What theory about ecosystem diversity and stability discussed in lecture do the statistics about rainforest species numbers given on p. 131 seem to support? *(Remember, rainforest physical environments are famously stable)*

5. What is the most bizarre rainforest creature that you've ever heard of? Your instructor's favorites include: bird-eating spiders; Eusocial (hive) spiders (S. American); and *canairu*, tiny catfish that can swim up the urethras of large mammals unwise enough to go swimming in the Amazon *(They have spines on some of the fins that work like harpoons, complicating removal. Yes, humans are large enough)*

6. p. 131 talks about the forest as a "cornucopia of undiscovered food sources [and] compounds with seemingly magical properties." Does anyone have any idea (or guess) about the percentage of the U.S. pharmacopoeia derived from botanical sources?

7. How could development that forces indigenous peoples to relocate make it more difficult to identify potentially useful drug sources in the rainforest?

8. If the soils under rainforests are really so "nutrient-poor... that elsewhere [they] would not even support weeds" (p. 132), how can lush jungles can continue to exist on them?

9. Where might you find rich soils in the tropics?

10. Describe the social and ecological cycle that leads from "urban slums to Amazonian slums" (p. 134). What do you think is the main difference between this cycle and traditional slash and burn agriculture, which has been shown to be fairly sustainable?

11. Why do abandoned agricultural fields carved out of the Amazon rainforest often wind up in the hands of ranchers? (p. 134)

12. Describe the debate concerning road-building in the Amazon. What might governments of Brazil and other nations do to prevent "uncontrolled development" from accompanying road building (p. 135)? How does this situation compare to road building and development in America?

13. A transamazonian highway crossing into Peru would give access to the rainforest to what nation that causes environmentalists the most concern? Why be concerned?

14. How well have the dams built in the Amazon basin performed at generating electricity? (p. 136) So, why would the Brazilian government persist in wanting to build more?

15. (p. 136) What are some reasons to hope that the rainforest won't completely disappear?

16. Have you encountered any sustainably harvested products such as those described at the bottom of pg 136? What market forces or political changes do you think will be necessary to help these products become accepted as an alternative to cutting forests?

17. The section titled "What can Americans Do?" contains the suggestion that policies proposed by America to stop the destruction of the rainforests must involve sacrifices on the part of America as well. What kind of environmental demands might the Brazilians feel the right to make of us, in exchange for taking our demands related to their treatment of the Amazon rainforest seriously? Try to come up with some specific ideas for policies which would fit this more equitable model.